Dr. Breath
THE STORY OF BREATHING COORDINATION

by Carl Stough
with Reece Stough

Carl Stough is Dr. Breath. He probably knows more than any other man about the body's most important, and perhaps most ignored, function—breathing. And it is this knowledge that enabled him in the early 1960's to discover breathing coordination, a discovery of revolutionary proportions in the field of health.

This discovery defined for the first time the proper function of the human respiratory mechanism and opened a new approach to the interrelationship of the respiratory system with the several systems of the body, particularly the nervous system. From it, Carl Stough was able to devise The Stough Method of Breathing Coordination, which has already profoundly altered the lives of those fortunate enough to have been taught it and which will ultimately, it is hoped, through its world-wide dissemination bring improved health and longer, more relaxed lives to all human beings.

In *Dr. Breath*, Mr. Stough writes of his many-faceted career, from his earliest interest in the link between breathing and the production of sound, through his intensive work in the field of medicine (particularly with advanced emphysema patients), his crusading against air pollution, to the discovery of breathing coordination and its consequences. The story is

DR. BREATH

The Story of Breathing Coordination

told within the framework of his experiences as respiratory consultant to the 1968 United States Olympic Committee.

As the adventures of a layman in the world of medicine and subsequently in the world of sports, this book makes exciting and fascinating reading. But its value transcends the pleasure it may bring. As a report on the vast potential of breathing coordination, it is indispensable.

Photograph by Bradford Bachrach

CARL STOUGH was born in 1926 in York, Pennsylvania, and now lives in New York City. He is the founder of The Carl Stough Institute of Breathing Coordination, Inc., a non-profit organization for research and education in the field of breathing. Mr. Stough is married and has one daughter. His wife is co-author of this book.

Dr. BREATH

THE STORY OF BREATHING

COORDINATION

by Carl Stough

with Reece Stough

William Morrow and Company, Inc.
New York, 1970

WITHDRAWN
by Unity Library

UNITY SCHOOL LIBRARY
UNITY VILLAGE, MISSOURI 64065

Copyright © 1970 by Carl Stough and Reece Stough

All rights reserved. No part of this book may be reproduced or utilized in any form or by any means, elec-
tronic or mechanical, including photocopying, recording
or by any information storage and retrieval system, without permission in writing from the Publisher. Inquiries
should be addressed to William Morrow and Company,
Inc., 105 Madison Ave., New York, N.Y. 10016.

Printed in the United States of America by
American Book–Stratford Press, Inc., New York, N.Y.

Library of Congress Catalog Card Number 73-119847

This book is for our beloved daughter,

      LEE,

without whom it would never have been written.

TABLE OF CONTENTS

7

Contents

8

Prologue

THE ELUSIVE QUARRY

In the year 1968, while continuing pursuit of the elusive quarry I have sought for the better part of a lifetime, I had the privilege of serving the United States Olympic Committee as respiratory consultant in preparation for the high altitude competitions of the XIX Olympiad in Mexico City. I came into that position through circumstance which created for me an unusual profession and resulted in an unusual discovery.

The elusive quarry I have pursued is no common variety of game; it is, rather, answers to the many problems involved in the seemingly ordinary, taken-for-granted act of breathing. Far from being ordinary, the act of breathing is a transforming potential, as the following account of several phases of my pursuit of the elusive quarry will indicate.

Prologue

THE ELUSIVE QUARRY

In the year 1968, while continuing pursuit of the elusive quarry I have sought for the better part of a lifetime, I had the privilege of serving the United States Olympic Committee as respiratory consultant in preparation for the high altitude competitions of the XIX Olympiade in Mexico City. I came into that position through circumstances which created for me an unusual problem and resulted in an unusual discovery.

The elusive quarry I have pursued is no common variety of game; it is, rather, solving to the many problems involved in the seemingly ordinary, taken for granted act of breathing. Far from being ordinary, the act of breathing is a transformation potential as the following account of several phases of my pursuit of the elusive quarry will indicate.

DR. BREATH
The Story of Breathing Coordination

1

DR. BREATH

On certain afternoons in the spring of 1968, visitors to the fieldhouse at the Yale University track in New Haven, Connecticut, might have read this cryptic legend scrawled across the bulletin board:

DR. BREATH IS HERE TODAY!

And they might have heard the colorful comments of athletes trying to unriddle words which only the initiate could have interpreted.

The first time I saw it, I was transfixed. I felt that it should convey some sort of meaning. A second reading stirred up a vague restlessness at the back of my mind. The third time around delivered the message. Being quite alone at that moment, I could afford to risk my dignity with loud, soul-satisfying laughter.

"Dr. Breath is here today!" I struggled to recover my composure and get on with my business. Marvelous how five simple words could reduce high purpose to absurdity. I wondered whose creative mind had produced that sparkling wit.

Before I could clear the fieldhouse, a group of athletes burst in and paused to skim the bulletin board for the instructions of the day. The "Dr. Breath" baffled them as completely as at first it had me. I could have solved the mystery for them, but I decided to let them do that for themselves. I went on out to the track and left them to their speculations.

"Dr. Breath," I repeated. Who but a supposedly serious undergraduate could have come up with that one? I remembered that I was supposed to be serious, and I knew that I could never again be quite so serious as before my encounter with the fieldhouse bulletin board.

I was Dr. Breath.

Undeniably, the title was descriptive, if inaccurate. I was not a doctor of any kind nor was I likely to be one. However, always mindful of small blessings, I determined to take my medical degree in good grace. I might have dreamed of many things in the course of my life, but certainly one of them was not a medical degree conferred upon me at Yale University. Although I would forego its use in public, I was pleased nonetheless to have received it. It told me all I needed to know about my work at Yale. I had a nickname. I was no longer an outsider to be viewed with suspicion.

Suspicion, skepticism did not disturb me. I had grown accustomed to a certain amount and was prepared to accept it as one of the hazards of my profession. However, I was always glad to be past it, because it made my work unnecessarily difficult.

Compared with what I had been doing, the project at Yale was pure pleasure. Still, a vestige of reservation hung in the atmosphere. I did not need a quantity of imagination to tell me what the uninitiate were thinking, nor did I begrudge the initiate their polite hesitation. My activities looked silly when observed from a distance, and they seemed silly at the outset to the person with whom I worked.

But now that I had been dubbed "Dr. Breath" in all the grandeur of the fieldhouse bulletin board, I was in. I had made it over the psychological hurdles. Dr. Breath could go forth to meet the challenges of the afternoon, secure in the knowledge that for once the odds were in his favor.

As my new title indicated, I dealt with the process of breathing. Since there are many methods of breathing and many exponents of each of the methods, the mere mention of breathing is likely to prompt a humorous dismissal or a heated controversy. The subject is delicate, possibly because very little scientific exploration has been conducted in the field. Breathing is too obvious to arouse much curiosity, and curiosity is the soul of investigation.

Most of my adult life, then some twenty years, has been concerned with the process of breathing and its effects upon the various actions and reactions of individuals. For ten years I had been working with the breathing problems of the desperately ill, and for seven years I had been engaged in a medical study at the West Haven Veterans Administration Hospital in West Haven, Connecticut. The afternoon of my elevation to the brotherhood of the fieldhouse elite I had just come from the West Haven VA Hospital, where I had been working with patients in the advanced stages of emphysema. I looked forward to my encounter with the young athletes, whose problems were less complicated.

For several weeks I had been coming to Yale to work with select members of Coach Robert Giegengack's track team. I was engaged in an unusual athletic study of breathing efficiency for my own organization, The Stough Institute, in cooperation with the United States Olympic Committee, whom I served as respiratory consultant. The project was one of mutual interest. The Institute wanted to find out as much as possible about the respiratory condition and habits of athletes at the peak of condition, and the USOC wanted to know to what degree an athlete might benefit from the use of a new method of breathing called SIMBIC or "breathing coordination."

My job for the Institute was to examine the respiratory processes of the subjects at the outset to determine any faults or irregularities in the breathing mechanism or the breathing pattern. That done, SIMBIC instruction could begin. Faults and irregularities could be corrected as the instruction proceeded and the subject developed his coordination. The end product of such training and development was maximum efficiency of breathing achieved with minimum effort. Observations and exchanges throughout would indicate the effect of the breathing in other than strictly respiratory areas. The information so obtained would later be correlated with other material to build toward broader understanding of breathing in relationship to total body function.

The Olympic Committee was interested specifically in increasing breathing efficiency. The specter of high altitude breathing problems was troubling the sports world as the time of the 1968 Olympic Games in Mexico City drew nearer. Increased breathing efficiency would enable athletes to provide their bodies with an extra margin of energy that could mean the difference between victory and defeat. If SIMBIC supplied that extra margin of energy, one of the problems would be solved and, in all likelihood, several others along with it.

My earlier work in athletics had turned out some interesting results, which I hoped to reproduce at Yale. My original theory was that by breathing with maximum efficiency and minimum energy expenditure the athlete could reduce the time required for warm-up and recovery. To everyone's amazement, including my own, the benefits of breathing coordination spilled over into wholly unanticipated areas. Athletes and coaches involved in the initial studies were elated to find that performances invariably improved as soon as a certain stage of development had been reached. SIMBIC could not give anyone an ability he did not already possess, but it could enable him to use his ability to his full potential.

The temptation to emphasize the increase in performance ability brought about by breathing coordination was great, but I decided on a course of resistance. Performance improvement is an immediate, indisputable advantage and certainly a gratifying one. However, it should not obscure the long-range benefits in terms of health and well-being. I was as pleased by the disappearance of muscular spasms and nervous stomachs as I was by the appearance of new records. I hoped that SIMBIC would become a way of life for my trainees, not just a means to an immediate end.

When the incorporation of breathing coordination into the Olympic High Altitude Training Program came to consideration, my chief concern was in the area of recovery. I had observed that in recovering from performance, athletes tended to adopt the same breathing characteristics as those the emphysema patient exhibited. Enough emphysema patients who had been former athletes had come to me for SIMBIC instruction to convince me of a link between emphysema in later life and excessive demands on the respiratory mechanism in youth. The decreased oxygen content of the atmosphere at high altitude would compound greatly the normal problems of recovery.

The pilot study at Yale involved a quantity of planning and expense for the Institute; therefore, I was particularly eager for it to go well. The key figure in the undertaking was Robert Giegengack, head coach for the 1964 Tokyo Olympics and then vice chairman of the Men's Olympic Track and Field Committee. Breathing coordination results with athletes had already convinced the Olympic Medical Training and Services Committee, headed by Dr. Merritt Stiles, then USOC second vice president, of the value of incorporating SIMBIC instruction into the high altitude program for the Olympic candidates. The final decision, however, lay with the coaches. The object of the Yale project was to demonstrate with action what at that time, to any practical-minded coach, amounted to little more than hearsay. Coach Giegengack's skepticism was understandable. He had to pass judgment on an intangible that might be influenced by any one of a number of factors.

If I had been advocating the use of a new-model track shoe or some form of equipment, I could have tested my wares at Yale. If they had proved to be successful there, I could have shipped them across the country for other coaches to try with their teams. Each coach could have judged my product on its merits as he saw them, and a decision to accept or reject could have been reached easily enough.

Unhappily, such was not my good fortune. I was not demonstrating the merits of track shoes. No tangible product was involved. I was attempting to introduce a new idea: that manner of breathing was of vital importance both to the athlete's performance and to his health and general well-being. Furthermore, the new idea involved a number of complexities, not the least of which was a new method of teaching. To carry the complication one step more, only I could teach the new method.

It was not humanly possible for me to go on a crosscountry

teaching jaunt. I had commitments which kept me in the Northeast and would have necessitated constant commuting. Even if a venture of that nature had been possible, time had run out. Although Dr. Stiles and I had been considering and working toward the project since 1966, a series of setbacks had delayed it. We seemed to have moved from one cancelation or postponement to another.

Originally, the exploration of the possibilities of breathing coordination was to have begun in January of 1967, using the Yale swimming team as subjects. Had the outcome been favorable, a follow-through with other Olympic coaches across the country would have been scheduled. Ironically, Professor Robert Kiphuth, the mentor of the USOC, died two days before the meeting set to discuss my proposals for procedure. He was an important figure in my particular area of operation, and his sudden death necessitated many revisions in Olympic planning. What should have been completed in the spring of 1967 had to be postponed until midwinter of 1968. Nothing more could be done about it.

When midwinter of 1968 finally came around, Coach Giegengack agreed to let me work with his trackmen. He was familiar with the preliminary athletic studies and with the medical background of SIMBIC and was ready to try anything that might be good for his athletes. I realized very soon how fortunate I was to encounter a man so willing to give a new idea a chance. His initial skepticism did not influence his observations and evaluations.

The instruction schedule had to be tight because everybody's time was at a premium. I projected ten individual instruction sessions for each man over a period of five weeks. At the end of that period a valid evaluation could be made and future procedure could be determined. "Gieg," as the Yale men called him, approved this schedule.

Considering how the instruction began at the "Cage," the Yale indoor track, I would not have been surprised by anything that might have happened. It is a tribute to the courtesy of the track team that I survived the first session. Although Gieg had a conventional office elsewhere, at the Cage his informal "office," so termed by the track wits, was a set of high steps against the wall, from which vantage point he could keep an eye on everybody and everything. My own office was of similar informality: a table a few feet away, in full view of every passing runner.

Time and circumstance had made me a master of improvisation, and I was not given to shyness; even so, I did usually have a certain semblance of privacy in my work. But if that could not be, it could not be. Before I could think twice, Gieg had summoned a runner and introduced us. As we proceeded to my office, the young man was politely attentive, and the atmosphere of the Cage became charged with curiosity.

I knew how ridiculous the next scene would appear, and I could guess how foolish my first subject was sure to feel. As briefly as possible, I explained purposes and procedure, then I asked him to lie down on the table. Only a split-second of hesitation and he stretched out full-length under the questioning gaze of his teammates. Silently, I accorded him a share of the pity I was meting out to myself.

Palpation, or touch, is essential in determining the existing state of the respiratory muscles and the structure of the chest. Having no alternative, I began to move my fingers lightly over his chest. The corner of his mouth twitched uncertainly. I could have sounded the unvoiced question: *This* is breathing instruction? The only indication of anything out of the ordinary, though, was a few protracted seconds of awed hush before the effort to restore normalcy began.

First sessions are an unknown quantity. Progress depends upon the physical and mental state of the subject. I had not hoped for much progress in my initial public appearance at the Cage, but I might have spared myself this pessimism, for my young man was completely receptive and responded quickly to instruction. When I could feel his body relaxing beneath my touch, I knew the battle was half won. Absurd as the maneuvers may have appeared to onlookers, breathing coordination had been established and the subject was aware of the change within himself.

At the end of the session he slid off the table and stretched. "I never felt so relaxed in my life," he announced jubilantly to the apprehensive trackman next in order.

The beginning was over! By the end of the afternoon the inner circle had gathered about the table to watch my final session with Team Captain Mark Young, who had an obvious breathing problem and exhibited serious, unsuspected breathing faults. While I corrected his breathing pattern, his teammates kidded him mercilessly.

"Hey, Mark! You're not even breathing," someone called.

"How do you manage to get around the track? Think you can finish today?" needled another.

Their easy humor assured me that I was well on the way toward my goal. Later Gieg's satisfied expression confirmed my belief. The seeming handicap of my private office in public view had proved its advantages. Because each of the runners could see for himself what was happening to the others, instruction became progressively easier. The reserve had vanished by the time I got to Mark and I was able to work with him much more effectively than I might have been in other circumstances.

After two sessions I could discern the improvement in breathing and the steady response to the coordinated pattern. The athletes were attending my instruction sessions faithfully and doing their best to incorporate the new mode of breathing into their total daily activity. The speed of their development astonished me. Their bodies were so well-coordinated to begin with that they were able to achieve quickly the new coordination of the respiratory muscles.

By the third sessions the athletes themselves could identify a change in habits and sensations. One discovered that he had been holding his breath in class, particularly during examinations. He also confessed sheepishly to abandonment of his practice of taking sugar cubes and "over-ventilating" prior to racing, a futile and dangerous folly often exercised in the hope of gaining extra energy and oxygen. (Gieg's face took on an explosive purple hue when he learned of this secret sin.) Another found that he no longer had trouble falling asleep at night. A third noted relaxation of customary tensions. Still another, an asthma sufferer plagued by dust irritation, reported pronounced improvement in his condition.

Soon after these subjective improvements began to appear, Dr. Breath came into being. No one ever addressed me in that fashion, but if anyone had, I would not have been offended. I accepted the title as an indication of rapport, which is extremely important to the learning process.

That point marked the end of the introductory phase of the Yale project. Subjective improvements were increasing from session to session, all reservations had been removed, and degrees of improvement were noted in performance. I had not worked in the field of athletics long enough to make any kind of predictions. On the basis of my experience in other areas, I knew what was reasonable to expect. I would just have to wait to see whether my expectations would be fulfilled and whether that fulfillment would be sufficient to influence the decision of the Olympic coaches.

2

WHAT IS IT?

Waiting—for transport, people, events—has been one of the few certainties of my life. As a matter of preservation of sanity, I have had to learn to wait creatively. When nothing I can do will hasten the desired result, I try to use the time between to advantage. While I was waiting for the Yale athletes to develop their breathing coordination, my mind kept turning to a familiar problem that I had not solved to my complete satisfaction. I decided to work on it as a worthwhile diversion.

In teaching a new pupil breathing coordination, I generally follow a more-or-less regular pattern. Since most people are rather vague about the respiratory system and its functions, a brief description of what breathing involves is the starting point. After that comes an outline of procedure, then I set about establishing breathing coordination.

Once breathing coordination is established, I can say with complete aplomb, "There you are. That's breathing coordination."

Having just transferred from one state to another, the pupil has the experience of a distinct sensation and can say wisely, "Oh."

25

Chances are that he will not pursue the subject further at this point of learning. He knows from his personal experience what breathing coordination is and in what way it is different from previous experiences and sensations. Until he has progressed to a much higher stage of development, he is not likely to ask himself, or me, for a definition and explanation of breathing coordination. Even then he will be satisfied easily because he will be dealing with a known factor.

The unknown provokes curiosity and leads to pursuit of satisfaction. The person who has not experienced breathing coordination is the one who poses the question "What is it?" That is a forthright question which merits a forthright answer. Denied a forthright answer, the questioner may well doubt the validity of what he cannot experience for himself. For some time prior to the Yale project I had been trying to define and explain SIMBIC for those whom I could not teach. I wanted to nail down with unmistakable terms all the elusive ideas compounding breathing coordination. Therein lay my problem. It was quite large enough to occupy the waiting gap in the Yale project.

Breathing coordination can be defined very readily, but it cannot be explained with matching ease. Part of the difficulty arises from a lack of appropriate terminology. SIMBIC is new. The terminology having to do with respiratory functions carries with it overtones and implications which create prejudice and obscure the ideas presented. New terms have had to be invented to convey the new thought in breathing.

"Breathing coordination" itself is a new term conceived to embody the thoughts, observations, and conclusions of two decades of investigation of the human respiratory process. By definition, breathing coordination is breathing in that individualistic pattern which engages all the muscles of respiration, both voluntary and involuntary, and provides the most efficient deflation and inflation of the lungs with the least amount of effort.

People have been breathing for a long time, for so long that no one pays much attention to what he is doing. Breathing is equated with being alive, and like being alive, it has been left to the sages to ponder. Philosophies have centered about breathing. The profundity of breathing is honored in the commonplaces of everyday speech.

Clichés abound. How many people have "caught their breath" in surprise? How many patients have been told to "take a deep breath"? Those who run will surely be "out of breath." Anything of great import is "the very breath of life." Children used to "hold their breath" to bring round stubborn parents and nurses. The matchless beauty of the heroine takes away the hero's breath. On the other hand, her "bad breath" can take away the hero himself.

Everywhere, constantly, people are breathing. It is the first thing they do when they come into the world. It becomes a habit. When they break the habit, they very speedily depart or expire—"breathe out," that is. Yet, from the first breathing in to the last breathing out, few think about their breathing unless it troubles them. Even those who deal with the act of breathing are often ignorant of the mechanics of breathing and the functions of the respiratory system. Conversely, scientists who deal with the mechanics of breathing and the functions of the respiratory system seldom have much time to spare for investigation of the act of breathing in relationship to its influence on the whole individual.

Breathing is the unknown quantity separating life from death. It is the major function of the respiratory system. It requires the use of both voluntary muscles, those which can be controlled at will, and involuntary, those over which no control can be exercised or which can be influenced only indirectly by other muscles or forces. In the act of breathing the muscles compel the lungs to contract and expand to move air out and in. Once the air is taken into the lungs, various physiological processes occur, but they do not fall within the province of breathing.

Breathing coordination deals strictly with the movement of air out and in the lungs. As the term implies, it has to do with the working together of all the muscles involved in the act of breathing. A normal, healthy infant is born with breathing coordination, with his own particular pattern of breathing in which the muscles function synergistically to produce a greater flow of air out and in the lungs than could be achieved by any other pattern. Somewhere along the paths of childhood he will lose his breathing coordination for one reason or another.

Work with hundreds of children over a period of more than fifteen years has revealed the loss of breathing coordination as early as the age of two-and-a-half years. Follow-up studies have failed to show a single case of permanent restoration. Often, physically well-coordinated persons, athletes in particular, will happen upon breathing coordination and will identify it as "getting the second wind." Others will fall into it by chance and will experience a high sense of well-being. When the original pattern has been lost, the probability of regaining it permanently is remote. Although the sensation may be remembered clearly, the knowledge necessary to achieve it is lacking. No routine has yet been developed to enable an individual to arrive at breathing coordination without the aid of a skilled instructor.

When breathing coordination is lost, it would seem to be lost forever, except for occasional, fortuitous restoration over short periods. Happily, life depends not upon breathing coordination, only upon breathing. The body's marvelous ability to compensate weakness in one area with strength in another keeps the respiratory muscles functioning in spite of any stress or damage. Since altered breathing patterns have served the human race through the ages, it would be a little foolish to suggest that they be jettisoned now.

The difference in breathing in the coordinated pattern and in an altered pattern is the difference between operating at peak efficiency and just getting along. An engine does not have to be in tip-top condition to work, but it gives a better performance if it is. When the breathing potential is fulfilled, potentials in other areas are fulfilled; hence, the importance of breathing coordination to athletes, especially. The body's energy derives from the oxygen in the air breathed; the more efficient the breathing, the more oxygen will be delivered to the body. Breathing puts gas in the tank, so to speak, and it is wise to keep the pump working.

Although the muscles of breathing will not of themselves return to the abandoned coordination of infancy, they can be trained to function again in the original synergistic pattern of breathing coordination. A person who has been properly instructed and who can exercise self-discipline can maintain his breathing coordination indefinitely. Breathing coordination is a physical discipline which must be constantly attended, as any skill must be.

The muscles of breathing cannot be brought into the individualistic pattern of breathing coordination by the exertion of force, either that of the voluntary muscles or applied external force. They respond only to light external pressure in combination with the pressure of the air within the lungs.

Herein lies the distinction between breathing coordination and the many, varied schools of breathing techniques.

Exponents of the various systems of breathing deal, knowingly or unwittingly, with the voluntary muscles, which can be controlled at will and can effectively influence the passage of air out and in the lungs. Since most people breathe at the lowest level of the body's demand for oxygen, anything they do to improve their breathing habits is worthwhile. Thousands of people who adhere to a breathing regime can attest that they feel better when they pay attention to their breathing and are soon aware of a change for the worse when they neglect it. Everyone has had the refreshing experience of taking several "good, deep breaths." Breathing is the most important act in life. To neglect it is unwise.

In contrast to the other systems, breathing coordination bears significantly upon the involuntary muscles. Lying as they do beyond the control of the will, the involuntaries respond to the stimulus of the total respiratory condition at any given time. Just as the digestive processes of the stomach and the beat of the heart cannot be willed into action, neither can the involuntary muscles of respiration. They must be activated by a delicate balance of pressures within the respiratory system. The maintenance of that delicate balance is one aspect of breathing coordination.

Because of the body's ability to compensate weakness, breathing goes on in spite of any damage sustained by the respiratory mechanism. Respiratory injuries can remain undetected for a lifetime and can produce endless, baffling complications. In the process of establishing breathing coordination, respiratory damage and faults become apparent and can be managed effectively.

For the well who are in good physical condition, almost any

means taken to improve breathing habits will pay dividends in good health. Those who are in poor health or who suffer respiratory disease or disorder should take great care in the method followed to improve their breathing. Practices which impose undue stress on any part of the respiratory apparatus are suspect. Where there is existing weakness, they can cause damage; where there is already damage, it may become more so. No one would consider attempting to run with a broken leg, nor should anyone with respiratory damage consider vigorous exercises calculated to improve breathing. The resulting harm to weakened areas would outweigh any small measure of good.

Encounters with young and old, sick and well have made me acutely aware of the prevalence of respiratory problems and the ramifications of respiratory disorders. Quite apart from confirming statistics, I have observed a steady rise in respiratory complaints since the late 1950's. The increasing pressures and tensions of a highly commercialized society have produced corresponding pressures and tensions within the body. Body irregularities manifest themselves almost immediately in the breathing. Knowing the key role that breathing plays in the interactions of the body systems, I have become more and more concerned by the seeming indifference of the influential to the need for research and education in the field of breathing. Nothing exceeds in importance how and what one breathes. All of life's problems halt abruptly when breathing stops. Yet, practically anything else is given precedence. At one extreme is the individual who would rather die of emphysema than give up smoking. At the other are the industrial interests, large and small, that befoul the air in the name of commerce and for the sake of the economy.

If any doubt exists as to the increase in respiratory irritation and infection, a visit to any public place and notation of the number who cough or clear the throat or labor at breathing should dispel it. After the opening of the Verrazano Narrows bridge between Brooklyn and Staten Island, the incidence of respiratory infection in one Brooklyn community tripled within the first six months. Engine exhaust from the increased flow of traffic through the community robbed the residents of their health. Respiratory infections have a cumulative effect. Most respiratory patients exhibit a background of infections and illnesses. From such minor occurrences major difficulties arise, because these seemingly minor irritations inflict a certain degree of damage every time they occur.

After the confirmation of the discovery of breathing coordination in 1964, my concern for the general indifference in the field of breathing had reached such a degree that action became imperative. In the late fall of 1965 The Stough Institute was incorporated under the laws of New York State as a non-profit membership organization with tax-exempt status. The manifold purpose of the Institute was designed to include research and education in the field of breathing, development of methods of improving breathing habits, and stimulation of thought and interest in the field. At that time the medical study of emphysema was in progress at the West Haven VA Hospital and occupied my attention entirely. When that particular program went into the final phases several weeks later, I could begin to think about projects for the new Institute. So much needed to be done that I hardly knew where to start.

For a number of years my primary interest had been in the breathing problems of the chronically ill, principally emphysema sufferers. I was thoroughly familiar with the breathing patterns and habits of the most hopeless of the advanced emphysema patients. I was equally familiar with the faults and irregularities of the well. Having seen two-thirds of the respiratory spectrum, I had a gnawing curiosity about the other third, the physically superior. I had worked with sportsmen and knew that their tendency to possess a higher degree of physical coordination than most enabled them to adopt a new respiratory pattern very readily. I wanted to find out whether the superior athlete in top form had retained the rare ability to breathe in his original, perfectly coordinated pattern.

Breathing was a topic of considerable interest to the world of athletics even in the early winter of 1966 because of the anticipated problems of breathing in the high altitude of Mexico City at the 1968 Olympic Games. When I asked Dr. Merritt Stiles for permission from the USOC Medical and Training Services Committee to audit projected symposia on breathing, he became interested in SIMBIC and its possible application to Olympic team candidates. The eventuality of Institute research work with Olympic candidates arose. Pleasing as this development was, it implied a necessary delay in moving through official channels, and I was eager to begin the athletic study.

Although I had never worked with athletes seriously engaged in competition, I felt certain that SIMBIC instruction would be of advantage to them. What I was not so certain of was its effect on the training program and possible interference with performance timing. While I was waiting to hear from Dr. Stiles, I decided to undertake a preliminary study to quell my uncertainties. I got in touch with Coach Frank Stellato of the Boys' Clubs of New York, a former coach in all sports at West Point Military Academy, and outlined my proposal to him. He was enthusiastic.

At the outset the main object was simply to determine the effect of SIMBIC on the athlete's warm-up and recovery. My theory was that increased efficiency of breathing would reduce warm-up time and conserve energy for performance. Similarly, recovery time would be cut. The young athletes assigned to the breathing program were the club's finest. One was the Golden Gloves champion; another, a Golden Gloves runner-up. All participated in track and basketball. They had had no form of breathing instruction previously and were not aware of a particular pattern of breathing either under normal conditions or during sports participation. They seemed to be in excellent condition.

My first shock came when SIMBIC instruction began. Their physical condition belied their respiratory condition. Far from being in the superior state I had expected, they all exhibited respiratory faults and weaknesses in varying degrees of seriousness. However, their basic muscular coordination enabled them to learn rapidly, and after the emphysema patients, working with them was a joy.

The next several weeks were a series of shocks and revelations. All my preconceived notions about the respiratory condition of athletes were shattered. I was particularly disturbed when I found that the stress of recovery after extreme exertion throws the athlete into an aberrant pattern of breathing, for such stress over a period of time could cause irreparable respiratory damage.

On the positive side, SIMBIC exhibited the anticipated effects of releasing tensions and improving general health. Warm-up and recovery times were reduced significantly. These results alone would have been sufficiently gratifying, but there was also the big, beautiful bonus of improved performance. My apprehension that changing breathing patterns might disturb performance was unnecessary. Other dramatic, positive results of the study combined with the respiratory findings swept aside any hesitations I might have had about the benefit of SIMBIC to the athlete.

My interest in the Olympic candidates became twofold. Not only was I curious about their breathing patterns and habits, I also was convinced that breathing coordination would provide a very definite health and safety factor at high altitude and that it would exert a favorable influence on performance. I sent off a report on the preliminary athletic study to Dr. Stiles with the notation that SIMBIC could be incorporated into athletic training programs with considerable benefit.

Additional investigations in the field of athletics strengthened my convictions. When Dr. Stiles notified me of my appointment as respiratory consultant to the Olympic Committee, I set about formulating plans for projected instruction programs and was hoping to be able to begin immediately. No sooner was all in readiness than the delays set in, and I was still waiting in the spring of 1968, the Olympics only months away, to do what had for me become a sort of obsession.

3

OVER THE SHOULDER

Often, as I shuttled between the West Haven VA Hospital and the Yale track, from one extreme of my interests to the other, I experienced a momentary loss of identity and had to ask myself: "Who are you? What are you doing here?"

Who was I indeed? To my Yale men I was the amiable Dr. Breath who appeared at appointed hours, performed a few mystic rites, and somehow enabled them to convert the air they breathed into physical power. To my West Haven men, all advanced emphysema patients, I was their last hope, a kind of combination Svengali–Simon Legree who could keep them breathing after everything else had failed. To myself I had become an enigma.

During the ten years prior to 1968 I had moved so swiftly from one new situation into another that I had hardly had an opportunity to adapt to one before another was thrust upon me. Unsuspectingly, I had entered a world totally foreign to me for what was to have been a limited visit and had remained indefinitely. I was still there—more at ease, to be sure, but never at home. A layman in the world of medicine is like a mouse in a cage of tigers. I had not been devoured, but the roaring had often rattled my bones. Frequent glances over the shoulder were necessary to reassure me that the cage had a door through which I had entered, by invitation, and through which I could leave, by choice.

Looking over my shoulder into the past, I am always startled by the number of situations to which I have had to orient myself quickly in spite of my confusion. Among the worst was my first day at the East Orange, New Jersey, VA Hospital. I have become accustomed to hospitals, but I never will like being in them, in any capacity. That day was something of a trauma. Had my faculties not been entirely numbed, I probably would have turned and walked out into more compatible surroundings. I remained, however, and in all innocence launched into the impossible.

Early 1958 marked the beginning of an adventure I never could have anticipated. Dr. Maurice J. Small, chief of tuberculosis service at the East Orange VA Hospital, was looking for some form of breathing therapy to aid pre- and post-operative TB patients. Concurrently, a New York organization with which he was associated was seeking to extend the range of services provided by its therapists. My work in the area of breathing was familiar to the group, for I had achieved a reputation as an innovator of breathing technique for the production of sound. I was asked to try to develop a method of breathing instruction for the ill which therapists could be taught to practice. I agreed.

My ignorance of the nature and complications of the disease was total. For several weeks I spent long hours in the medical library, and Dr. Small assured me of any aid I might require. The respiratory mechanism can readily be damaged by misuse as well as by abuse. I did not want to risk inflicting further damage upon those who had already suffered too much. I prepared myself as best I could and bravely set out for East Orange.

The antiseptic atmosphere of a hospital alone was enough to jar my courage. The politely aloof reception of my future colleagues served to complete the job. When I got to the patients, I was operating on reflexes developed over the years of teaching. Somehow I survived my introduction into the alien world of medicine and went on from bad to worse.

Within a short period I learned through the hospital underground that the physical therapists were grinding their axes because of a conflict of methods. Having no desire to bring discontent into the physical therapists' camp, I was happy when Dr. Small suggested abandonment of the original project. I would gladly have gone back across the Hudson to Manhattan, but he had other plans to propose. Nothing was being done for emphysema patients; therefore, he reasoned, I might as well have a try with them. Anything that could be done to help relieve their breathing difficulties would be of value.

Emphysema was a word which then had not yet found its way into the general vocabulary, certainly not into mine. I went back again to the library and I conferred with Dr. Small to learn as much as I could about something nobody seemed to know very much about. Heretofore my objective had been to get air into the lungs. In dealing with emphysema I found that I was expected to get it out, for emphysema is a condition in which air becomes trapped in the lungs and cannot be expelled as in regular breathing.

Feeling somewhat at cross-purposes with myself, I let my interest in breathing lure me from the relatively tranquil world of the well into the troubled atmosphere of the desperately ill. The first patients assigned to me were all bed-patients in advanced stages of emphysema. They had been given every medication known for the disease and been written off as hopeless. No one really expected anything to come of the project, for at that time emphysema was considered the end of the road. These men had reached the dead end. I could not succeed, for there was no way to restore lung tissue. Nor could I fail, for the disease itself was the final failure. I could hope only to help.

When I began to teach the emphysema patients how to breathe, two facts were foremost in my thoughts: these men had lost their ability to breathe in an effective pattern and their breathing mechanism was severely damaged. They could not tolerate excessive exertion of any kind. Whatever was done for them would have to be done without force and with great care. If I had been cautious, I would have let well enough alone, but I had become curious. There were many things I wanted to know.

I particularly wanted to know why the emphysema patient's chest was raised. Upon inquiry, I was told that the raised chest compensated weakness in other areas of the respiratory mechanism and was a characteristic of the advanced stages of the disease. The raised chest disturbed me endlessly because I knew it to be so wrong and I wanted to put it right. I used to go home from East Orange and observe the regular breathing of my infant daughter as she slept. Her chest rose and fell effortlessly in a perfectly coordinated pattern. When I placed my hand upon her chest, I could feel the muscles relaxed beneath my touch. That was what I wanted to feel when I placed my hand on a patient's chest. Instead, there was the tensed knotting of muscles laboring exhaustingly to perform the act of breathing.

Finally one day I could no longer resist the temptation. As I was talking quietly with a patient to help him relax, I put my hand on his chest and applied a little more pressure than usual to try to make the chest descend into a more nearly normal position. To my amazement, I could detect a slight relaxation of the taut pectoral muscles and an ease in the breathing.

"Can you feel that?" I asked quickly.

He nodded. As I continued to apply gentle pressure to the upper chest, the relaxation continued and the breathing eased. I followed the same procedure with the other patients, who responded similarly. I realized then that for these men I could not use the devices employed to teach the well. They lacked the physical ability to assume attitudes and follow verbal instructions designed to produce certain effects on the breathing mechanism. They were supine, which fact alone necessitated a different approach, because the respiratory system responds differently in the different physical positions and my instructions were geared principally to the upright position. Talking to them was not sufficient; I would have to rely on touch. Unlike the well, they had no memory of the sensations of easy breathing.

When I agreed to accept the East Orange project, I thought naïvely in terms of adapting regular instruction procedure to the particular needs of the individual. Each session with a bed-patient who could hardly speak above a whisper and who might be taking oxygen throughout the session made increasingly clear to me the need to develop an entirely new method of teaching the technique of efficient breathing. I had not considered this possibility. However, I was not expected to succeed. I had been asked only to try. The least I could do was that. My misgivings were legion.

I have wondered often what I might have done at that point if I had not had my infant daughter to serve as a norm. I strongly suspect that I would have abandoned East Orange and that my career would have gone quite another way. Constant observation of her breathing at rest kept firmly in my mind the impossible goal toward which I had to guide the emphysema patient. Comparison between the perfect and the imperfect supplied a gauge of progress.

Little by little I came to recognize the distinguishing physical characteristics of the emphysematous chest. I also noted that the breathing difficulties and physical irregularities differed from patient to patient and that each had to be dealt with according to his differences. By some instinct which I could not possibly explain, I was compelled to apply gentle pressure to any part of the chest which was not functioning in a normal pattern. The muscles always tended to respond and breathing became easier. With light palpation of the various areas of the chest I could establish a pattern of easy breathing similar to the regular pattern of my daughter. Once the patient had learned to recognize the feel of the new pattern, he could breathe without my aid until he began to move or to speak. As fast as I solved one problem, another arose.

Inquiries about the effect of speech and motion on the patients' breathing failed to elicit from my medical colleagues either explanation or theory. Mine was a carefully supervised, strictly do-it-yourself job. I did my own theorizing and arrived at what now seems a simple, common-sense answer: the respiratory muscles were too weak to support the increased breath demands of speech or motion, and the stress of effort caused the patient to lose the new breathing pattern. Next question.

The next question followed with horrifying rapidity. How could those muscles, some of which did not function properly, others of which could not be controlled, be strengthened? Again the answer was obvious: by exercise. Next question. This one was a real challenge. How do men lying helplessly on their

42

back and totally lacking the energy for any exertion perform exercises? The answer came swiftly: they cannot. This left me exactly nowhere.

Since exercises were impossible, the only thing I could think of was to encourage the men to talk while I continued the light pressure over the stress areas of the chest. The procedure worked well enough, but I was so busy trying to figure out what was happening physically that I could not be attentive enough to keep up a running conversation. I also noticed that as the men tried to think of something to say or drifted to a painful subject, they tended to tighten the muscles. I began to make up sentences for them to repeat and added words and phrases as their ability to extend the exertion increased. I encouraged them to follow the practice between sessions, always striving to keep the sensation of the easy breathing achieved with my aid. To my utter amazement, it worked!

Soon the patients began to give indications of improvement. The signs were not dramatic, but they were there. I could detect a loosening of chest muscles, with slight lowering of the shoulders, and various patients reported sleeping better. Some who had had difficulty eating were able to swallow with greater ease. One patient who was living on six liters of oxygen a day began to decrease his consumption. Another who had been bedfast was able to get up and move about.

From time to time doctors and therapists came to me smiling. "What are you doing to those emphysema patients?" they inquired. "I hear you're having great success. Even getting old Frank down on the oxygen. Great!"

They went away scowling because I could not tell them a single thing. I honestly did not know what I was doing to get a response where others had none. I know now what I was doing, but then I was venturing into the unknown. I was too occupied with immediate concerns to reflect and analyze and correlate. I was constantly learning from the doctors and nurses and from the patients themselves the peculiar psychology, the needs, the paralyzing fears, and the complicated problems of the emphysematous.

My manner of teaching was continually developing toward a definitive method. After a patient learned to maintain his breathing pattern in a supine position, he had to be taught to maintain it sitting, then standing, then moving about. Every increased demand on energy affected breathing and required an adjustment to the new situation. I had to find a way to make the necessary adjustment. When a patient reported the effectiveness of some personal experimentation, I passed the information along to the others. Depending upon the consensus, I incorporated it into my teaching or filed it as a good suggestion for given circumstances. One suggestion in particular developed into an important teaching device.

Although the use of contrived sentences to produce sound had achieved a gratifying measure of success, I was not wholly satisfied with it. I cast about for something better but found nothing. When a resourceful patient told me he would rather count than recite sentences, I decided to use numbers with the other men. They were approved unanimously and in the course of time have been elaborated into a precise method for physical development and for the measure of degree of development. To many they have become a distinguishing characteristic—or perhaps *idiosyncrasy* is a more accurate word—of my teaching method.

Not long after the introduction of sound as an exercise device for my emphysema patients, their improvement became dramatic. They could tolerate more physical exertion and perform tasks which had been impossible for them previously.

One elderly man who had not been able to walk across the room not only could walk but could walk up the hospital stairs, a remarkable feat for an advanced emphysema patient. Several developed to such a stage of self-management that they were discharged from the hospital and could go back to moderate work. A doctor told me that a patient under his care had shown a marked improvement in coronary condition. Ulcers of long duration began to disappear. The patient who could not breathe comfortably for more than fifteen minutes without oxygen was able to go without it for as long as eight hours and could get out of bed and move about the hospital. He astonished the nurses by pushing a wheelchair along the corridors for support and balance to help maintain his breathing pattern while walking.

Perhaps the most dramatic episode was that involving a fifty-five-year-old patient who had suffered the advanced stages of emphysema for eight years. After his discharge from the hospital he undertook to pilot a boat down the Inland Waterway from New Jersey to Florida. A violent storm caught him off the Carolinas, and he spent the long night battling the raging wind and waters. The following morning he had such a severe attack of dyspnea (breathlessness) that he was rushed to a Charleston, South Carolina, hospital for emergency treatment. By the time he reached the hospital, he had regained control of his breathing sufficiently to refuse oxygen therapy. Instead, he insisted upon being left undisturbed for a short while. During that time he was able to recover himself by use of the system we had worked out for just such an emergency, and he walked away to continue the journey to Florida. This was a man who had exhausted his private resources in search of relief from the terrible breathlessness of emphysema and who had come to the East Orange VA Hospital as a last resort.

In the beginning each success brought a flurry of enthusiasm from the hospital staff, and a few more patients were shunted to me for instruction in breathing. Dr. Small was quick to note the improvement, but he could no more account for it medically than could I. The improvements simply would not show up in the standard tests. In one report he commented, "We have a hunch that many of the tests we are utilizing are rather gross for our purposes." While I worked with him, he never gave up the hope that whatever I was doing could be delineated and defined precisely.

His charity, however, was not equaled by others of my colleagues. I could sense about me a building atmosphere of hostility, and I suspected that many a difficult patient was sent to me in the expectation that I would fail. My situation was not eased by my ignorance of the physiological effects of my overt actions. I could and often did describe in detail what I did in instructing a patient, but I could not explain why those particular actions produced such phenomenal results in respiration and so many assorted side-effects. The description without an explanatory follow-up provoked a state of intense irritation. Everyone felt that I was hoarding a secret. No one would believe that it was a secret even to me.

Finally my chain of success snapped and the atmospheric pressure dropped accordingly. One of my patients who had made significant improvement contracted pneumonia and had a great deal of difficulty with his breathing afterward. I could not help him regain the ground he had lost during his illness. Working with him became problematic because of his constant complaint of abdominal pain. His doctor could find no cause for the pain and could devise no cure. Meanwhile, the pain continued and I kept trying.

For some reason I felt that my inability to help this patient was connected with my inability to explain what I was doing. I had been causing something to happen within his respiratory mechanism. Now, a change within him since his illness was canceling what I did and making impossible the occurrence of that inexplicable something. Quite by accident I noticed that his lower abdomen protruded when he talked. I placed my hand upon it as he continued and pressed lightly to make it descend with his speech. A few sentences later he became aware of a lessening of pain. In a short period of time his pain disappeared and his improvement resumed.

Again I had stumbled across another piece in the respiratory puzzle that my teaching of the diseased had become. This one I could explain. The diaphragm had not risen into the pulmonary cavity as it should have when the patient exhaled. It had descended erratically into the abdominal cavity, thereby creating in the lower abdomen pressure which in turn caused pain. I could now identify a weakened diaphragmatic muscle immediately by the protrusion of the lower abdomen upon the exhale.

Enough clues had accumulated by merest chance for me to realize that I was on the trail of something or other. I had next to no scientifically measurable data to present, but I hoped that the subjective and objective improvement of the patients would be sufficient to enable me to go on with the work that had begun so haphazardly.

So little was being done about the breathing problems of the emphysema patient in the late 1950's that any advance would be worthwhile. Mine was a halting advance; nevertheless, it had possibilities. I began to cast about for means of seeing it through to a logical conclusion.

4

THE WITCH DOCTOR

After a year-and-a-half in the East Orange VA Hospital with patients continuing to improve mysteriously, I became more and more self-conscious about my inability to explain what I was doing. I felt like some sort of witch doctor who conjured effects with strange numerical incantations. I am sure there were those who considered me closer to voodoo than to science. If I did not produce a few solid scientific facts soon, I might very well find all my work in emphysema jeopardized.

Whatever I had done for patients, I had failed to accomplish my primary task. I had not developed a teaching method which therapists could utilize, and my sponsors were becoming impatient. The two-year grant for the project was nearing the end. To receive another, I would have to have some indication of progress toward the assigned objective.

Chief stumbling block to progress was that I had no formula for altering the breathing pattern of the emphysematous. My management of every patient was different. I knew that something similar was happening to them all, but I had not the faintest inkling what it was. How could I possibly train anyone to teach when I could not tell him specifically

49

what he was to achieve? Going through a series of motions, which was all that I could describe, would produce haphazard results. At best, the patients would receive only temporary relief from their breathing difficulties; at worst, further damage could be inflicted upon the respiratory mechanism.

An unexpected turn of events rescued me from my dilemma. Some of my patients had been undergoing the standard tests for emphysema and showed an improvement over their condition prior to breathing instruction. Dr. Small wrote the magic words: "If additional studies in more of the patients now receiving instruction do show these small increases to occur consistently, they may give us a clue to significant improvement in some measurable parameter." On the strength of his report and the case histories of my patients, a grant was obtained for further investigation into the use of breathing patterns in the management of emphysema.

Time and again I heard, "What do you do that is so different from what everybody else does?" To all appearances, what I did was not drastically different from other approaches to breathing. Only the results were different. Depending upon the severity of the disease and the ability of the individual to discipline himself, those whom I had instructed could manage their breathing independently without artificial aids. Follow-up of emphysema patients who had been discharged showed many of them to be in better physical condition than before the onslaught of the disease. This was not true of other methods of breathing.

If, then, I could determine precisely what I did and describe exactly how I did it, I would have something to teach aspiring instructors. This happy thought served as a temporary relief from the pressure to begin training others in my own particular brand of witchcraft. To anyone not thoroughly familiar with the disease and its effect upon the respiratory system, my practices would be little more than just that—witchcraft—and just as unlikely to produce positive results.

For many, the end results of my instruction were sufficient. They were willing to concede that I must be doing something right. Others, however, were less charitable; some were openly hostile. The uncommon success of the East Orange emphysema project soon became well known enough for the editor of a pharmaceutical company's house organ to be interested in an article for his magazine. I was pleased because I hoped that awareness of the work being done might bring the support needed to intensify it. The article was prepared and submitted to hospital officials for approval. That was the end of it. Opposition to publication was too strong. The reason given was that the inevitable inquiries could not be answered for lack of sufficient scientific documentation and the hospital might be embarrassed. More than ever I felt like the weird witch doctor weaving his spell.

Even so, the luxury of self-pity did not tempt me long. I had learned that seeming dead ends can be turns in the road, to be approached more in curiosity than in despair. If scientific documentation would satisfy the opposition, then scientific documentation would just have to be obtained. Knowing the difficulties involved, I did not bother to ask myself how. Oddly enough, at that time the demand for proof of my work was a demand for analysis of the results rather than analysis of the means used to achieve the results. Conviction that I was stubbornly guarding a secret was so strong that the thought of analyzing my procedure did not occur. The main objective seemed to be to prove that the results had little or no scientific validity and that improvement which could not be measured on standard charts and graphs was no improvement worth the mention. I wondered how I could have generated so much furor when all I wanted to do was what I had been asked to do—help people breathe.

Early in 1960 the opportunity to extend the breathing instruction to the Naval Hospital in Philadelphia came about and I accepted it. There I worked with a group of Navy doctors who were very much interested in the effect of breathing techniques on the progress of emphysema and in the management of other respiratory diseases and disorders. Conferences with them taught me a great deal about respiratory diseases and disorders which I was able to incorporate into my own thinking. I had dealt only with emphysema and was not familiar with the many manifestations of respiratory damage. The knowledge was valuable.

Meanwhile, the work at East Orange continued. As my early patients came back for checkups, the long-range effect of their breathing instruction could be observed unmistakably. Their emphysema, which is an irreversible, progressive disease, had not progressed, but the standard tests failed to show results of appreciable significance. There was no way to measure the removal of the terrible fear of suffocation or to determine the vast consolation of being able to manage the breathing process unaided.

The Navy doctors were quite advanced in their approach to emphysema, and some of their comments set me to thinking about the standard tests. The chance remark of a patient that the tests exhausted him kept returning to my mind. While I was observing the tests one morning, I realized what was wrong and why the results were always a disappointment to me. The atmosphere of the entire procedure was one of tension, which is among the chief enemies of the emphysema sufferer. Tension builds into more tension, finally climaxing in breathlessness and the feeling of suffocation. No patient could put forth his maximum effort under such circumstances. The whole procedure was diametrically opposed to everything I taught. My objective was to teach the patient how to relax his tensed muscles so that they could function in a pattern of relaxed breathing. If he were tense, he could not breathe efficiently, and if he could not breathe efficiently, the test results were invalid as far as the measurement of my work was concerned. Moreover, the tests required forced breathing at maximum effort, whereas my patients were never permitted to force an exhale or to exert their breathing beyond the limits of ease. I suggested certain changes which were adopted with notable alteration of test results.

In another familiar area of tension I was not so inventive. The demand for trainees had become imperative. Although I was convinced of the futility of the undertaking, I agreed to begin the long-evaded task. I had had two years of intensive work and study in the area of emphysema, and all of that time had been required for me to become acquainted with the nature of the disease and the complicated problems of the patients. Beyond that, I had no ready formula of instruction to communicate. Yet I was expected to take trainees totally ignorant of the ramifications of the disease and the respiratory difficulties involved and to teach them an undefined method of instruction. If try I must, try I would. I had run out of arguments.

The trainees came and the trainees went, of their own accord. The complexities of dealing with the chronically ill were discouraging enough, but the highly technical approach to the process of breathing was too much. The trainees were accustomed to the relatively simple respiratory problems of the well who want nothing more than to extend their breathing capacity. To deal with a gasping bed-patient who might very well suffocate before the session ended was completely unnerving to even the most intrepid. They resigned, freely admitting that the job differed considerably from what they had expected. Paradoxically, a barrage of criticism was leveled at me for failing to do what I had already warned I could only fail to do because of the limitations of my present knowledge. Although I understood the frustration I had unintentionally aroused, it was no less unpalatable.

There had to be at least one, and there was—an aspirant who was convinced that his empathy and inborn sense of humanity was sufficient to plug all the gaps in knowledge. Far be it from me to shatter dreams. We set out together upon the pathway of emphysema headed in the direction of hope. The journey was not without mishap and misgiving, but we pressed on bravely. One fine spring day we came to the awesome citadel of the Philadelphia Naval Hospital and plunged directly into a conference with the doctors. On the schedule were some particularly knotty problems, and the discussion veered off into technical areas. I was called on for a number of decisions involving patient welfare and respiratory management. I was too preoccupied to notice my companion.

Later, when we had left the conference and were ready to begin our round of patients, he turned to me hesitantly. "There's no need for me to go on. It would just be a waste of time. I'd never get through one of those conferences."

His humility made me very sad, because he should never have had to humble himself so. His original confidence in his ability was entirely justified by what he had been told upon application for the training. No one who was not directly connected with the work could or would concede that it was in any way out of the ordinary. The case histories of my patients read like advertising copy for a potent patent medicine. They were unbelievable. So, nobody really believed them. That was a mistake discernible only in the field of action, as this latest training casualty had discovered for himself.

For a while after the Philadelphia episode there was a lull in the training demands. I could devote my thought and energies to the innumerable respiratory problems which my mere presence seemed to create. Patients were continually coming to me with assorted questions about the respiratory mechanism and the process of breathing. Their ignorance of their own bodies always surprised me, because I foolishly had assumed that everyone had at least a rudimentary knowledge of physiology. Even more foolishly I had assumed that a universal awareness of the importance of breathing existed. Nothing could have been farther from the truth.

Discussing breathing with the Philadelphia doctors one afternoon, I noted the general lack of information on the subject and asked why this was so. Why was the process of breathing not explained to respiratory patients and why were they not cautioned about the serious consequence of faulty breathing habits?

"Because most of us don't know that much about breathing," a brisk young captain replied. "We're too busy specializing in respiratory diseases and finding ways of treating them to think about breathing."

"Nobody ever thinks about breathing until he can't, I suppose. Then it's a little late. Sometimes too late."

"Do you know what you ought to do? You ought to go over to the University of Pennsylvania Graduate Medical School and talk with Dr. Arthur DuBois. He's in research and can give you some good ideas."

Forthwith, the doctor who had made the suggestion called

Dr. DuBois and arranged an appointment for me. Dr. Du-Bois received me graciously and listened attentively while I elaborated my work and findings. He took particular interest in my observations and conclusions concerning the effect of various breathing patterns on areas of the body other than the respiratory system. Suggestions he made during the meeting led me later into a series of research and study projects. If I had not met him at that precise time, my career would have been altogether different. He gave me some good ideas and prompted me to think in terms I had not considered previously.

Although the work at the Philadelphia Naval Hospital went well and I had a splendid opportunity to broaden my knowledge of the latest respiratory concepts and practices, the situation then existing within the hospital management was not entirely satisfactory. A rather rapid turnover of staff made the continuity of work difficult and necessarily consumed a lot of time in repeated briefings. Finally, a doctor with whom I often conferred advised a transfer of the Philadelphia program to the St. Albans Naval Hospital on Long Island. He pointed out that St. Albans Hospital had one of the largest respiratory departments as well as out-patient clinics on the East Coast and that it served all branches of the Armed Forces. It would be ideal for a continuation of the exploratory work I had begun in the application of my particular technique of breathing management to the management of emphysema and other respiratory complaints. The prospect was challenging.

By whatever mysterious communication system it is that keeps the personnel within a given field informed of activities within that field, accounts of the East Orange and Philadelphia projects had long since reached St. Albans. Before the subject was broached, St. Albans officials had entered a request for respiratory services as soon as there was an opening in the schedule. I regretted leaving my kindly colleagues in Philadelphia, but the trip from Manhattan to St. Albans was quicker at a time when I never seemed to have enough time. As fast as one thing ended, another began.

Just prior to the start of the breathing program at St. Albans Hospital, I was drawn into an area which I had not considered before. I was called upon to provide private breathing instruction for the ill. Private breathing instruction for the well is one thing; for the ill it is quite another. I was not certain that I wanted to place myself in so vulnerable a position. Doctors with whom I was directly associated in teaching patients and in exploring the possibilities of breathing in the management of disease never paused to consider my lay status. I knew my business of breathing; they knew theirs of medicine, and that was that. Other members of the profession, however, were often incensed by what they considered to be my poaching on the domains of medicine.

My investigations always remained strictly within the field of respiration, a legitimate branch of science. At no time had I ever suggested that breathing instruction could substitute for the medical knowledge and skill required to treat a diseased condition. It might aid in the management of a diseased condition, but certainly it should never be interpreted as a medical treatment for that condition. Nevertheless, I frequently encountered the animosity of doctors who refused to believe I accomplished anything out of the ordinary. My lack of standard scientific documentation and my inability to present a formula for teaching made me highly suspect.

Because of my work in hospitals, I had fallen into the easy habit of referring to those whom I taught there as "patients."

The well whom I taught were "pupils" or "students"; I interchanged the terms loosely. The ill were automatically "patients." Such verbal slips made in the wrong place could have unpleasant consequences. There were many who belittled me, but I did not believe anyone would go out of his way to harass me. Even so, I wanted all my activities to be open and well defined. I conferred with several doctors, and the consensus was that breathing instruction given in cooperation with the patient's doctor surely could arouse no objection. However, if the patient's doctor were not in accord, the patient might be caught in a dilemma detrimental to him.

With that solid advice serving as ground rules for operation I accepted as a pupil an emphysema sufferer referred to me by a former East Orange patient. Once I had begun to work with the man, I realized that he was opening for me a door into another room of the twilight house of breathing. His psychology was drastically different from that of the hospital patient. Since his psychology and his breathing were interacting forces, my approach and management had to be different. The hospital patient was recognized as being sick by virtue of being in the hospital. This man did not want to admit illness because it was a nuisance. He would overexert himself and inflict further damage rather than limit his activities. I had a new category to explore.

When the program began at St. Albans, I had many new categories to explore. The doctors in the respiratory department were highly receptive to new ideas and possibilities and proposed making the range of my work as broad as possible. I would deal not only with emphysema but with the management of all breathing problems. I would have a chance to study the effect of my instruction on every kind of respiratory disease and disorder. Laboratory facilities and the services of technicians were placed at my disposal, and I was free to consult with the medical staff of the respiratory department.

I had, in effect, a clinic for the handling of breathing problems. Here was my golden opportunity to obtain scientific documentation of my work. The facilities were much more extensive than those at East Orange and could carry my investigations much farther. The possibility was suggested that the breathing technique and the teaching method I had developed might be used as a standard procedure in the management of respiratory disease and disorder. That was an inspiring thought but it was a long way from realization. None knew better than I.

Before anything could become standard procedure, somebody had to find out exactly what it was and how it worked. After that, somebody had to find a way to train instructors who could make it available to those in need of it. A large order for somebody, especially when I was that somebody.

5

SEARCH FOR AN ANSWER

"How can anything so good cause so much trouble?" I often asked myself during the latter days of my tenure at East Orange when the controversy over my work had reached its zenith. An aura of the absurd hung about the stubborn insistence for measurable scientific proof of the improvement of bed-patients who could get up and walk and perform acts of which they had been incapable for years. Absurd or not, there it was and it would not go away when I closed my eyes. I counted myself vastly fortunate to have at St. Albans Hospital the means to search for an answer to the questions posed by my entry into the respiratory field. The outlook for the future was encouraging.

Despite the frustrations encountered at East Orange, a significant achievement had come out of the work there. What had begun merely as a service to try to ease the discomfort of the emphysema patients had developed into a distinctive breathing technique with an equally distinctive method of teaching. Of all the breathing techniques employed to relieve the breathlessness of respiratory conditions, this was the only one that enabled the patient to breathe without artificial aids and to maintain himself independently—some

patients took care of themselves for as long as six months without seeing me—once he had mastered the technique. Moreover, a follow-up of patients showed enough incidence of arrested progress of the disease to warrant the hypothesis that the breathing technique had caused the arrest.

In both East Orange and Philadelphia the efficiency of the technique had been demonstrated repeatedly. At neither place, however, had a concerted effort been made to describe it or to find the means of teaching it. The East Orange doctors wanted scientific documentation of results; whereas the Philadelphia doctors, though personally interested in my theories and accomplishments, were professionally interested only in the solution of their patients' immediate breathing problems. At St. Albans I would have for the first time the complete professional cooperation required to conduct a proper investigation of the breathing technique I had developed over a period of two years of work with scores of advanced emphysema patients.

While I was cheering myself with that thought, two painfully practical matters presented themselves. Again, money was running out and I would have to do my share toward obtaining more for the continuation of the work. My sponsors had entertained a singular displeasure with me in the wake of my failure to fulfill the initial commitment to train teachers. They were not concerned with scientific progress or advance of knowledge and did not permit themselves to be persuaded easily to invest in either. For a bleak interlude the financial crisis hung like a thunderhead on the horizon before resolving and freeing me to attend to the other matter.

The other matter had to do with scientific procedure. Following Dr. DuBois' suggestion, I had begun to think in terms of a controlled study series to settle a number of issues and to find answers to the questions that had been plaguing me since my first patient showed signs of improvement. In my most recent forage for funds, I had secured a sum of money for just such a study, but I had not completed the necessary arrangements. Although St. Albans offered me splendid opportunity for independent research, it was not geared to controlled study. I had to look elsewhere.

When I had had occasion to discuss my work in emphysema with Dr. James Meneffee of the Duke Medical Center in Durham, North Carolina, he mentioned the possibility of interesting Dr. Nicholas D'Esopo of the West Haven Veterans Administration Hospital in such a project. I approached Dr. D'Esopo with my proposal and, intrigued by the potential, he agreed to undertake it.

Preparation for the study took me into the technical area of respiratory function that lay beyond the scope of my knowledge. I needed advice on tests and testing procedures most likely to provide the scientific data required to document my work satisfactorily. Another of Dr. DuBois' many courtesies had been to refer me to Dr. André Cournand and Dr. Harry W. Fritts of Bellevue Hospital in New York City, whose work in the respiratory field is classic. I conferred with Dr. Fritts and received his expert answers to the procedure problems. His interest and encouragement heightened my own enthusiasm for the complicated enterprise my work was fast becoming.

My first eight months at St. Albans were concurrent with my final months at East Orange. All the while, I was arranging for the long-sought project at the West Haven VA Hospital and seeing emphysema patients referred to me by people with whom I had worked or by doctors who knew of my work.

The small snowball of East Orange was generating an avalanche.

When the medical study began in West Haven in April 1961, my association of more than three years with the East Orange VA Hospital ended. So much had happened to me at East Orange that I came away with a distinct sense of leaving behind some essential part of myself. I had seen men die there of the various complications of disease. I had seen others who had given up hope go out into a new life. Most important, I had carried my interest in breathing into an area of great human need and had received an opportunity to make a contribution of knowledge in a field far too long neglected.

Leaving my East Orange patients was like abandoning trusting children. Some of them were in too advanced a state of illness to hope for more than relief from the sensation of breathlessness; others were well able to take care of themselves if they applied themselves. By this time I had worked with more than a hundred advanced emphysema patients, and I was certain that most of the East Orange men could get along without me. The purpose of my instruction was to enable them to regain control of their breathing and learn to manage themselves independently. In final reassurance, I told them to get in touch if ever they needed me. That was the weapon they required in the relentless battle against the terror of breathlessness.

When the study began at West Haven, the program at St. Albans had been underway for some time and proved to be an excellent supplement. The St. Albans doctors and technicians worked in close cooperation with me, and we were able to obtain much corroborative data. The subjective-objective results of the breathing instruction were exactly what I might have predicted from experience. As soon as the breathing patterns had been changed and developed, improvement was dramatic. Although the doctors were familiar with the earlier results, they invariably were surprised to observe similar results in their own patients. As always, hearsay was one thing; personal observation was another. Enthusiastic from the start, they became even more so with the continuing improvements the patients showed.

Because the respiratory department and out-patient clinic at St. Albans were extensive and accessible to all branches of the Armed Services, all sorts and conditions of men were shunted to the clinic set up for the handling of breathing problems. I saw such a wide variety of respiratory sufferers that I eventually reached the stage in which nothing perturbed me. I was mentally prepared to deal with anyone. Or, at least I thought I was until I walked into my office one afternoon and found an attractive, middle-aged woman sitting there quietly waiting. Very definitely I was not mentally prepared for this.

The Veterans Hospital had conditioned me to think in terms of men as victims of respiratory disorder. The thought that women, too, suffered respiratory complaints never occurred to me. Simple-minded, but true. For a moment I was nonplussed, then habit took over and tended the routine, while I considered the next move. I had instructed women in breathing technique, of course, but those women had all been well, and my instruction had been verbal. This unsuspecting woman would be the first upon whom I exercised my new technique involving palpation. I was concerned not so much for myself as for her. I wondered how she would react. Since I had no alternative, I continued the routine and asked her to lie down on the examining table.

"Of course, Doctor," she replied and promptly did as she was bidden.

To her this was as impersonal as fitting a pair of shoes. Relieved by her offhand response, I explained to her that I was not a medical doctor but a respiratory specialist who would teach her a new pattern of breathing to relieve her dyspnea, or state of breathlessness.

She accepted my explanation but persisted in calling me "Doctor," as did numerous patients and many of the hospital staff who had difficulty learning the pronunciation of my name. She was the wife of a naval officer, therefore was eligible for hospital services. Like my first private pupil, she prompted me to consider my work from a new angle and to reexamine some of my concepts. From her I learned more about the effect of tension on the emphysema sufferer. Her responses to instruction were different from those of most of the men I taught, and I was impressed again by the influence of multiple factors upon the respiratory system.

Not only did I learn to teach women from the officers' wives who came to the clinic, I also broadened the range of application of my breathing technique through the variety of respiratory diseases and disorders I encountered. The St. Albans doctors were interested in the practical application of the technique and assigned me a new problem every time one arose. Men came to me with chronic bronchitis, lung damage from tuberculosis scar tissue, asthma, lobectomies, whatever might affect the respiratory system and make breathing difficult. The approach to each condition had to be different, but the results were always the same. As soon as a certain point of development of the new breathing pattern was reached, the breathing improved and the condition itself showed improvement.

I grew accustomed to seeing all stages of respiratory disease and could recognize a respiratory sufferer almost at a glance. One of the curses visited upon the diseased is that the undiscerning eye fails to notice anything unusual, and even an advanced emphysema patient can pass for normal among close friends who do not know of his condition. The trained eye, however, reads the signs and identifies the patient. When an erect young Marine presented himself to me for breathing instruction, I looked him over and mentally questioned his presence. He proved to be a remarkably novel case.

As he told me of his background, his distress and tensions became evident in his inflection. He had been in service for some time and had wanted to reenlist for another tour of duty. He enjoyed athletics and kept himself in prime physical condition by taking part in a number of sports. He had noticed that he got a little winded occasionally after particularly vigorous activity but thought nothing of it. Then he had gone for his reenlistment physical examination. The medical examiner announced to him that he had advanced emphysema, and before the bewildered young man could identify his condition, he was shipped immediately to St. Albans for treatment and possible medical discharge. The intensity of his emotion almost broke through his Marine discipline. I could believe his account, but I could not bring myself to believe his emphysema. Nevertheless, I began instruction.

His manner of breathing indicated that some kind of irregularity was causing the sensation of breathlessness. I conferred with his doctor, who was as puzzled as I. A series of conferences with other doctors yielded no solution to the mysterious malady. After several instruction sessions, the breathing difficulty showed marked improvement. Still, no consensus could be reached on the nature of the respiratory disorder.

Nor was a definite decision ever agreed upon. The staff remained divided pro and con emphysema. The young man simply refused to accept any form of illness. The desire of his life was reenlistment. He applied himself faithfully to the development of his new breathing pattern, and his respiratory condition improved accordingly. Within a few months he surprised everyone except me by passing his medical examination for reenlistment in the Marine Corps.

Working with him made me wonder about the effect of faulty breathing plus constant, excessive exertion upon the respiratory mechanism. At East Orange I had had a few patients who had been professional athletes in their youth, but at that time I was too busy with the urgencies of the moment to search the past for causes. Now I knew a great deal more about respiratory problems and was beginning to think in terms of causative factors. Among my St. Albans patients and my private pupils were former sportsmen and athletes. Someday, I promised myself, I would look into the breathing patterns and habits of athletes and examine their respiratory condition.

Time and again emphysema patients came to me with long case histories of recurrent pneumonia and respiratory infections which had inflicted irreparable damage upon the tissue of the lungs, resulting finally in emphysema. For a while neither the doctors nor I gave the matter particular attention. A new breathing pattern was developed; the patient improved and in due time was discharged.

When an ex-Flying Tiger of the Second World War was admitted to the hospital and his emphysema was found to have resulted from extensive lung damage caused by "walking" pneumonia, we all paused to consider. This man physically could not afford to have another case of pneumonia, but he was in such a state of susceptibility that he could very easily go into another from a slight cold. He worked with me regularly and made steady progress in his respiratory development. He was kept under careful observation so that any infection could be treated immediately. The precaution was unnecessary. Within six months his condition had improved enough for him to be discharged. We later learned that he had become a detective.

We all decided to become detectives and make an investigation into the effects of breathing patterns upon the incidence of respiratory infection. A check of old cases and observation of new ones indicated a correlation, whereupon the doctors began to talk enthusiastically about exploratory projects and introduction of breathing instruction into the area of prophylaxis. I was very much pleased by their enthusiasm, but I could not undertake any more projects, tempting as they were. I should have liked to. There were many things I wanted to do and would have done if only I did not get tired.

Work at the St. Albans breathing clinic became so generally known that doctors from other hospitals in the vicinity came to confer and to observe. I was called upon frequently for demonstrations of my management of breathing problems. With each new group I always hoped that there would be some wise one who would know and could explain the technical complexities involved in my actions. There never was. Although the process of breathing involves both anatomy and physiology, neither branch of science has claimed it for thorough exploration. It was a little-known territory waiting to be mapped and charted. If I wanted a map, I would have to make my own.

Sometimes the zeal of my St. Albans colleagues was overpowering. As the numerous side-effects of the breathing technique on other systems of the body were noted, a resurgence of interest in prophylaxis occurred and a plan was devised to bring the high-ranking service personnel to the hospital for a regular program of instruction. I was flattered but not particularly happy. So much of my time was already consumed by instruction that I often chafed at the slow advance of the research. Furthermore, experience with older service officers had taught me to approach them with a certain degree of trepidation. Try as I would to ease around the problem, there was no way to avoid imparting the unwelcome information that their method of attaining their military posture was detrimental to breathing efficiency. I had had a variety of reactions. After the atmosphere had cleared and communication could be reestablished, I explained that the abnormal raised position of the chest placed the respiratory structure out of alignment and made proper functioning impossible. The point was conceded as instruction got along, but I did not relish the thought of indefinite repetition of the experience. Shortly after the start of the program a crisis in Washington brought it to a close. I had no regrets.

I never regretted having more time available, because something was always waiting to be done. With the aid of the various technicians and the cooperation of the doctors, I had been able to utilize testing procedures that Dr. Fritts had suggested. The results of the tests were exciting. They were providing the long-sought documentation needed to differentiate and establish the breathing technique I had developed. At last there was visible proof of the extraordinary occurrences within the respiratory mechanism brought about by the change in breathing pattern. I had a firm support for my theories and conclusions. I had escaped the narrow confines of subjective-objective reports.

Most dramatic of the earlier documentation were the inhale-exhale X-rays. Before beginning instruction the patient was X-rayed on the inhale and on the exhale. After a given period of instruction he was X-rayed again in the same fashion. The two sets of X-rays were superimposed to determine the motion of the diaphragm in performing those respiratory functions. They showed quite clearly an increased excursion of the diaphragm that could have been brought about only by the strengthening and developing of the involuntary muscles through the change in pattern of breathing.

The standard medical opinion then was that involuntary muscles cannot be developed. If I thought for one moment that contradiction of standard medical opinion is a desirable contribution to science, I could not have been more remote from reality. I had fallen squarely into a hornets' nest and was in danger of being stung to death. Once more, those who were there to witness accepted the evidence. Those who were not, refused to believe that what had happened either had happened or could happen. The diaphragm, I found out too late, was sacrosanct in the field of medicine. It was governed by established laws and would not suffer tampering, certainly not by an intruder upon the profession.

The previous controversy I had aroused was naught compared to this. Almost anybody who could spell *diaphragm* had a great deal to say. Conventional thinkers made mincemeat of me. Doctors and professionals who had heard of my work at second and third hand were not averse to belittling it. A high time was had by all.

As time does, that time, too, passed. I was shaken, but not for long. Other areas in my research were opening, and I was constantly coming upon new ideas to incorporate into my teaching and thinking.

6

EXPLORING NO-MAN'S-LAND

When I entered the medical world, I had already done a quantity of research in breathing for my own personal interest and for use in teaching the well how to breathe more efficiently. I had observed the breathing habits of hundreds of people of all ages, noting their common tendencies as well as their uncommon aberrations. I was fully aware of the influence of breathing habits on individual health and well-being. One point, however, had long troubled me. Nowhere could I find a complete definition of "correct breathing."

Many activities require excessive use of the lungs in their performance, and most of those who engage in them have an individual concept of "correct breathing." Certain cults achieve physiological and psychological effects by a controlled breathing which limits the supply of oxygen to the body. There are advocates of "belly breathing," "diaphragmatic breathing," breathing through the mouth, breathing through the nose, breathing through the pores, and to its exponents each form of breathing is correct. As far as the maintenance of life is concerned, any form of breathing will do.

More and more I came to think of the act of breathing— the manner in which the muscles are engaged to move air out and in the lungs—as a no-man's-land waiting to be explored and concealing who knows what discoveries to be made. The process of breathing was to me like a mountain. Each person had his own view of it, and each was so content with his own view that no one had bothered to explore the mountain to discover its true nature. Teaching had often shown me that what was "correct" for one was not necessarily so for another. Yet, I reasoned, everyone has the same basic respiratory equipment; there must be a common factor. In spite of my efforts I could not determine that factor.

Before I began to teach the chronically ill at the East Orange VA Hospital, I had no way of knowing how deranged the human respiratory mechanism could become and continue to function. As I taught and the men began to show improvement in the ease of their breathing, their pattern of breathing tended to resemble that of the well. I was convinced that a common factor existed and, if ever discovered, could be used to remedy the respiratory faults which lead to or complicate disease and disorder.

Not until the superimposed X-rays at St. Albans did I have a chance to look inside my patients and see what was occurring there. The most maddening aspect of work in the field of breathing is the extreme difficulty of ever knowing precisely what takes place in the process of breathing. Internal examination of a live subject is problematic; of a dead one, futile. Being able to examine those X-rays and see for myself the positive effect of the breathing instruction amounted to a sort of conversion. I was no longer content just to teach and pursue the research for sweet knowledge's sake. I felt that I had picked up the trail of something very important, and I wanted to follow it to a logical conclusion. If it were my

74

"common factor," as I suspected it might be, I wanted to isolate and identify it and put it to work.

One of the hospital doctors, Dr. James Ledwith, shared my enthusiasm for my private project and set up special studies with his patients to explore the effects of the new breathing pattern on the diaphragmatic muscle. Although it was heresy at the time, the X-rays gave undeniable proof that the weakened diaphragm, characteristic of the emphysema patient, had been developed by the new pattern of breathing. The orthodox view was that development of involuntary muscles is not possible. Fortunately for me, the hospital staff with which I worked was not committed to orthodoxy. We all went merrily on doing what we were not supposed to be able to do.

Exciting as the X-rays were, they paled in comparison to cinefluography, a process of photographing the action of the diaphragm as the patient breathes and speaks. The cinefluography equipment had not been available in the early stages at St. Albans, and I had never thought so superior a means of documentation would be at my disposal. Dr. Ledwith introduced cinefluography into the studies, thereby enabling us to extend considerably our range of exploration and examination.

When I saw my first film, I was almost overcome with the wonder of witnessing the invisible parts of the body performing their specific tasks. I had served as the norm for the emphysema patients, and I felt very odd as I watched my own diaphragm rise and descend. Comparing the distinct line of my diaphragm with the diffused lines of the patients' diaphragms, I had a heightened concern for the liability of the weakened diaphragm to damage. The weakened muscle is not detected readily and can be injured further without the individual's awareness.

Cinefluography provided valuable documentation for my observations and served as a rallying point for avant-garde thought in the respiratory department. After the film-viewing sessions, which always provoked discussion, doctors and technicians lingered to exchange ideas. Often, passing doctors would join the group. For me, those discussions served as a university in miniature. I would go home in the evening, my head bursting with information and ideas. Never had I undergone so intensive a period of learning.

Early in my work with emphysema patients I had believed that I was doing something quite different from the usual practices, but I did not know what it was or how to describe it. For want of more explicit terms I referred to what I taught as the "new breathing technique." That served well enough for a while, but at best it was makeshift. It begged questions and sooner or later prompted the annihilating wit, "What's so new about breathing?"

The X-ray studies at St. Albans indicated that the "new breathing technique" was not only new, it was unique in its ability to do to the respiratory mechanism what, according to medical record, had never been done. Cinefluography verified further that it promoted the development of the weakened diaphragm in the chronically ill. Long-sealed doors were beginning to creak open in the general respiratory field as well as in my own field of breathing. The "new breathing technique" could not continue with so nondescript a designation. Something better would have to be devised.

Before 1961 was far advanced, I began to think earnestly about terminology. Finding a name for what I did was fraught with all the hesitations, reconsiderations, apprehensions, and assorted mental pangs of naming a child. My colleagues participated in the enterprise, and the mood ranged from the seri-

ous to the absurd. Greek and Latin dictionaries were dusted off
and searched diligently for an appropriate combination of
words.

"If 'dyspnea' means 'difficult breathing,' " one doctor reasoned, "wouldn't 'eupnea' mean 'good breathing'? Why
wouldn't that be a good name?"

"Because nobody could pronounce it," was the quick reply.

"Well, who can pronounce 'dyspnea'? But patients feel
better about having something unpronounceable. Ordinary
English doesn't make much of an impression."

There was more truth in that last observation than would
bear admitting, but the obscurity of root combinations was
not what was called for in an area already too obscure. The
name should carry within it a capsule explanation of the technique. Like any cautious parent, I did not want to saddle the
new with a cumbersome name which might later prove to be
a handicap. Once the deed was done, it could not be undone
easily. I culled my notes and thoughts for a solution.

Countless times I asked myself, "What do you do?" I could
describe the motions employed in teaching a patient to
breathe in a new pattern more efficient than his old, but I
could not find a name to encompass them. The more I
thought, the more I came to understand that the principle did
not lie in what I was doing. The importance of all my work
was what I made happen within the patient himself. The
question, then, was, "What happens?"

Although I was thoroughly familiar with the mechanics of
breathing, I was not about to rush in where the experts tread
lightly. The functions of the muscles of breathing have been
described insofar as is possible, and I could hardly add anything more to the description. Besides, I knew from observation that my technique did not require overuse of any muscle

or set of muscles. In developing the technique I had instinctively avoided placing unequal stress on any part of the respiratory mechanism. I had observed the easy breathing of my infant daughter at rest long enough to be certain unequivocally that the natural pattern of breathing employed the total mechanism in a mutually complementary action. Unequal stress on any part over a period of time alters the pattern and, depending upon the nature of the alteration, can injure the mechanism. My goal with my patients was always to restore the breathing pattern to the completely coordinated unit I knew it should be.

With such reasoning I could finally answer the question. What happened was that in the instruction of patients I brought all the muscles of breathing back into a coordinated pattern and relieved the stress on any one muscle or set of muscles. I taught coordination of breathing to produce a synergism far more efficient than overuse of any single muscle or muscles.

Well, that was what I taught. I still needed a name for it, a name to distinguish it from other forms of breathing. I could have called it "coordination of the muscles of breathing," but that seemed a bit long. "Breathing in a coordinated pattern" prompted the same objection. "Coordinated breathing" seemed much better, but this was not quite what I wanted. After a wearisome testing of sounds and meanings, I came around at last to "breathing coordination." That sounded right. That was the name!

"Breathing coordination" was introduced in the spring of 1962 and accepted immediately as the only possible solution to the problem. Within a few weeks the term had become incorporated into the vocabulary completely. Soon it was bandied about as if it had existed since Hippocrates. I smiled inwardly when someone who could not possibly have known its tortuous evolution referred to it with the offhandedness accorded standard medical practice. I hoped that someday it might become standard medical practice both in prophylaxis and in the management of respiratory and related diseases and disorders. That day, however, lay far, far in the future with a vast amount of work and research in between.

Giving the technique a name simplified many matters. The name seemed to clarify it and make it familiar. It was no longer a mysterious, unnamed something that I did. It was breathing coordination. When asked what I did, I could say directly, "I teach breathing coordination." Natural reluctance to display a lack of knowledge being what it is, I generally could count on that statement to spare me a tedious attempt at explanation.

Embodying the idea in a name made discussions easier for the doctors. Until the naming, an unavoidable personal aura had pervaded the new breathing technique. With my personality removed, breathing coordination could be considered and evaluated for what it was of itself rather than as something I did to bring about the phenomenal changes in the condition of the respiratory patients. The patients themselves seemed to be more at ease with a proper designation for their new mode of breathing. A name may not change the essence, but it has a marked effect on the human response to that essence.

Now endowed with the dignity of a designation, the studies in breathing coordination continued at St. Albans, and another effect of breathing coordination as singular as the development of the diaphragmatic muscle was noted. One of the characteristics of the disease of emphysema is the raised chest. In the struggle to breathe, anyone experiencing breathlessness will tend to use the muscles of the upper chest area, the pectoral and the neck muscles, to empty and fill the lungs. This tendency is called "accessory breathing," and despite its total inefficiency, it creates the illusion of immediately supplying the body's insistent demand for oxygen.

The emphysema patient constantly experiences that demand for oxygen and constantly satisfies it as quickly as he is able with accessory breathing. Reliance upon these accessory muscles gradually draws the rib cage upward from its normal position, causing in the sternum, or breastbone, the development of a protruding angle at the juncture of the upper segment. The sternal angle, as it is sometimes called, can alter permanently the pattern of motion of the rib cage.

Alteration of the chest was accepted as part and parcel of emphysema. Conventional thought was that such alterations were the body's way of compensating the weakness of various respiratory muscles and that once altered, the chest could not be changed. The altered chest was the unmistakable aberration of the emphysema patient at the East Orange Hospital which prompted me to use palpation in teaching breathing. My uncontrollable desire to return the raised chest to a more nearly normal position was the starting point of breathing coordination.

Complete attention could be focused on the upper chest when the flurry caused by recognition of changes in the diaphragmatic muscle had subsided. X-rays taken before and after instruction showed that the raised chest had been lowered into a more nearly normal position. By distributing the work of breathing among all the patient's respiratory muscles, breathing coordination had removed the excessive strain from the accessory muscles. As the tension was released over a period of time, the chest descended and the sternal angle became less pronounced. Such an occurrence was supposed to be impossible, but there it was on the X-rays. The potentials of breathing coordination were opening so rapidly that it very often was difficult to grasp their significance. They were almost too good to be true. This abundance of benefits aroused skepticism among those who had not participated directly in the breathing coordination studies.

One somewhat startling benefit of breathing coordination was improvement in the voice, which I had expected from the beginning and had observed at East Orange but which had been overshadowed by the more dramatic developments of direct advantage in the relief of breathlessness. The St. Albans doctors noted with interest the unmistakable voice improvement, because advanced emphysema patients often can speak only a few sentences at a time and the voice is weak and indistinct. When such patients can sustain speech in an appreciably louder and clearer voice, the change is obvious. Improvements in voice and speech are corollaries of the development of the muscles of exhale, particularly the diaphragmatic muscle. As the muscles are able to support the increased air pressure of speech without tensing or inverting, the voice becomes stronger and speech can be prolonged. The voice improvement of one seventy-two-year-old man paralleled his increased diaphragmatic motion as shown by cinefluography and the improvement of his performance of standard respiratory function tests.

The patient's ability to produce sound served a very practical purpose of which I had become aware only after my method of teaching breathing coordination had developed far enough for me to begin to explore cause and effect. I had asked my early patients to make sounds because that act sustained the exhale and achieved the desired end of moving air out of the lungs. From sound-making the system of counting evolved into a simpler means of prolonging the exhale. As I continued to observe the improvement in voice, I realized that the effort of sustaining the exhale provided a self-regulating force against which the diaphragm could act. The length of a single count, the volume of the voice, and the ability to repeat a count or to extend its length were all self-regulating stimulants for the diaphragm and the other muscles of exhale. The moment the patient tried to force the count or exhale beyond the ability of the muscles to support the exertion, the diaphragm moved paradoxically and the excess pressure showed immediately in the protrusion of the lower abdomen.

From the length of time a patient could count on a single exhale, I was able to judge exactly how much physical effort he could exert. I used his counting ability to determine his ability to maintain his breathing coordination in the various positions of the body—lying, sitting, standing, walking—and in the performance of physical tasks. The counting finally developed into such an accurate gauge of the patient's physical endurance that the St. Albans doctors required a checkout through the breathing clinic before a patient was released from the hospital.

Absorbed as I was by the varied developments of the St. Albans studies, I was for a time more or less inattentive to the ever-widening circle of controversy over breathing coordination. My happy unconcern had to end. Emphasis on the development of the diaphragm through breathing coordination eventually brought a spate of interest and inquiries from many exponents of the various schools of "diaphragmatic breathing," particularly in the field of music. Teachers of singing reasoned, understandably, that they had certain measures for strengthening the diaphragm. Why, then, should they not be eligible to teach the emphysematous how to breathe? Once more, the old question: "What do you do that is so different from what we do?" The answer might have been that work with the emphysematous was in the field of medicine, whereas their technique and thinking were geared to the field of music, and the two were worlds apart. That, however, was not a complete answer.

Although breathing coordination does promote the development of the diaphragm, that development is only one part of the total achievement. The unique aspect of breathing coordination is that it recognizes the individualistic pattern of breathing which distributes the work of breathing equally over the entire respiratory mechanism. In a period of time, the constant, undemanding use of weakened muscles enables them to develop gradually according to the individual's ability to produce sound without causing a diaphragmatic inversion. Exercises designed to promote exclusively the development of any respiratory muscle or sets of muscles hold the inherent danger of damaging weakened muscles and throwing the respiratory mechanism further off balance.

During the period the "diaphragmatic breathing" adherents were insisting upon the inclusion of breathing coordination instruction within their range of activities, Frank Chapman, former Metropolitan Opera singer and husband of Mezzo-Soprano Gladys Swarthout, came to me for private breathing coordination instruction. He had advanced emphysema and was particularly interested in the St. Albans work. Upon request he agreed to participate in certain phases of the program. His extensive knowledge of various breathing techniques made him especially alert to the similarities and differences of breathing coordination. After undergoing a series of instruction sessions and the subsequent physical improvement produced by breathing efficiency, he informed the doctors that breathing coordination was unique in his experience. Later, he confessed to me that he had expected to learn nothing new, but I was not offended. I had expected him to expect just that.

Interest in the work at St. Albans also brought a number of requests for demonstrations and discussions of breathing coordination. Because of the numerous benefits to respiratory sufferers, breathing coordination became a sort of beacon to persons and organizations dedicated to the relief of such sufferers. The hope usually was that teachers could be trained quickly and put to work relieving respiratory distress. Although breathing coordination was nowhere near the teacher-training stage, demonstrations occasionally were given for organizations interested in keeping up with the latest developments in the field. One such organization was the Queens County Chapter of the National Tuberculosis Association.

The demonstration was well received and widely publicized, because the national organization at that time was extending the scope of its activities to emphysema. Since I was not in a position to undertake any additional programs, I did not think of it further than to be pleased that it had been successful and had acquainted more people with the work in breathing coordination. Little did I know how much thinking I very soon would be called upon to do.

7

A BATTLE IS FOUGHT

In the early 1960's so much was happening in the various areas of my life that I seldom had the leisure to appraise my activities on the basis of their direct benefit to me. I had become caught up in the excitement of finding something new that was potentially of great value to the respiratory field. I had also had the infinite satisfaction of doing what I enjoyed doing. More than that did not concern me, and the cost in time and energy went undetermined. Occasionally someone suggested that my knowledge of breathing could turn a neat profit, but to my financial detriment, I had more scientific curiosity than business sense and I never got around to the profit.

Eight months after I began the program at the St. Albans Naval Hospital, the medical controlled study was started at the West Haven VA Hospital on a note of high enthusiasm. Results from East Orange, Philadelphia, and St. Albans had contributed to the optimism and interest with which the new project got under way. For the West Haven doctors the prime advantage breathing coordination afforded was that it enabled the patients to maintain themselves independently after instruction ceased. In other forms of breathing the patients reverted to their old habits when instruction ended.

If I had paused to think, I might have wondered why the West Haven staff paid little heed to the St. Albans documentation of the physical changes breathing coordination effected. Those busy days were not given to reflection; so, I launched blissfully into the study I had long desired and long sought. As originally planned, ten emphysema patients with varying degrees of disability were to be instructed in breathing coordination and ten similar patients were to be selected at random to serve as controls. The second group was to continue with the conventional regimen for emphysema. At the conclusion of a given time the two groups were to be compared to determine wherein my patients differed from the controls.

Numerous tests were to be administered to measure the extent of the differences. If the group instructed in breathing coordination showed improvement, the control group was to receive some form of breathing therapy, such as intermittent positive pressure breathing. I felt rather odd about going into competition with machines, but that was the way it had to be. So be it! Should man triumph over the machine—that is, should the breathing coordination group progress beyond the control group—there would then be a solid basis for considering breathing coordination for possible inclusion in standard practice for the management of emphysema and other pulmonary disorders involving the distress of dyspnea.

The study would continue for approximately two years. In the event that it proved the efficiency of breathing coordination in the management of emphysema, I stood to gain directly only the intense personal satisfaction of finishing the job begun in 1958 at East Orange. Essentially, I would be doing at

West Haven nothing that I had not done dozens of times at East Orange and Philadelphia and was still doing at St. Albans. The difference was the use of controls, which at that time seemed to be the approved procedure for testing the efficiency of a practice. I believed in the practice I had developed during the sometimes very long, always intense sessions with people whose every breath was a struggle. I believed in it and I was convinced that it could be of inestimable advantage to the medical world.

My belief and conviction, plus a total familiarity with hospitals and the ill, obscured for me the fact that I was a layman. I had been coming and going among medical personnel so long that I had little awareness of status. I reasoned rather simply: If in pursuit of my interest in breathing I came upon something of use to someone else, the someone else would be glad to receive what I had found. That was very simple reasoning indeed. Although I had many friends and colleagues in the medical profession, far more considered me an impertinent intruder upon an exclusive preserve. Even so, I could not persuade myself that a good idea would be suspect because it originated outside the profession. I interpreted the endless testings and retestings to be the cautious procedure requisite to scientific certainty.

The work in the hospitals preceding West Haven had been directed principally toward helping the patient. If the objective were achieved, that, supposedly, was sufficient. What I failed to realize at the time was that no one expected the objective to be achieved. When it was, great excitement ensued and the medical batteries were drawn up to test and measure and examine and try to determine what had happened. When the patient continued to improve and when those capable of sustained effort went on to maintain themselves without me, the excitement cooled and caution set in. Here was an unknown quantity. Valuable or not, it was unknown. Fortunately for me, I encountered enough unconventional thinkers who shared my curiosity to be able to explore beyond the limits of standard practice. While the cautious were flexing their skepticism, we were documenting the impossible.

West Haven was different. For all of the initial enthusiasm, the study was scientifically staid and was not given to the bursts of excitement which a new development occasioned at St. Albans. Dr. Robert G. Nims, medical supervisor of the work, indulged in as much latitude as was possible but not much was possible.

My patients at West Haven followed the familiar pattern. Within a few breathing coordination instruction sessions they showed marked improvement. The official hospital report read: ". . . surprisingly good symptomatic results from patients who had considerable respiratory disability. That is, patients believed that they were improved and attested that they could do certain types of activity that they had found impossible or very strenuous previously."

One of the patients who "believed" he was improving was a proud man who had been forced to sell his small business because of his physical disability. When all of his reserves—some seventeen thousand dollars—were exhausted, he entered the Veterans Hospital as a last resort and was unofficially assigned to the "hopeless" category. After a course of breathing coordination instruction, he was discharged from the hospital and was able to take care of himself.

At St. Albans we were documenting physical changes in the respiratory mechanism and employing the latest available equipment to do so, while at West Haven, hospital authorities were noting circumspectly "patients believed that they were improved." The incongruity of the situation might have provided some slight amusement had not so much been at stake. West Haven was the culmination of years of practice and thought in the field of breathing. I had been frustrated frequently by clashes with orthodox thinkers but never when the consequences might make further progress impossible.

After six months of steady improvement in the patients, the original controlled study was abandoned because "it was possible that a considerable part of the patients' improvement might be due to attention, encouragement, and increased motivation given to them by a dynamic instructor." I suppose I should have been happy to think of myself as such a large charge of dynamite, but I knew that the dynamite could very well blow breathing coordination sky high. I felt like a latter-day Don Quixote tilting at medical windmills, and I am sure that to many my lay findings appeared just as absurd.

To intensify matters already too intense, at that juncture the term "breathing coordination" had gathered about it a number of practitioners who reputedly coordinated the breathing. Although there could not possibly have been any likeness to my work, a distinction had to be drawn to prevent confusion. The distinction had to be obvious. Unfortunately, it also had to be made odious by the introduction of personality into an atmosphere supercharged with personality. No longer able to travel alone across the unexplored reaches of science, "breathing coordination" became for purposes of investigation "The Stough Method of Breathing Coordination."

The second West Haven study was to determine the maintenance of improvement after the period of instruction concluded. Previous investigators of various breathing therapies had found that upon conclusion of the instruction period the patients reverted to their former degree of disability. Although the ability of patients to maintain their improvement had been the very feature of breathing coordination to interest the hospital authorities originally, now it was to be investigated again. Two reliable social workers were assigned to interview the patients and elicit from them progress reports possibly more accurate and objective than I might obtain. There were then East Orange patients who were maintaining their improvement and holding jobs after having been hospitalized three years or so earlier. I wondered if ever an end to proving would come.

Because breathing coordination was a brand-new thing which I had come upon through years of thought and practice, experiment and study, no certificate could be awarded me to attest my qualifications to do what I said I could do and what I already had done hundreds of times before. In an age accustomed to certificates and diplomas and awed by titles and degrees, I cut a puny figure with my unadorned name. West Haven with its due process was my hope that once and for all the efficiency of breathing coordination could be established. Once established as standard practice, it could be put to work where it was needed and I could do something other than prove that it would work. A perfectly good medical tool would not be limited by the failure of its fashioner to have acquired a proper title.

The necessity of referring to my work as "The Stough Method of Breathing Coordination" was exceedingly unfortunate. The continual use of my name galled, and the study took on characteristics more of a trial than of an investigation. I began to ask myself if I were developing paranoia. At any rate, I built a high degree of oversensitivity when every success evoked question and further challenge. Long after the objective—maintenance of improvement—was achieved, the questioning of results continued. I appreciated the scientific caution and I wanted all doubt to be removed, but I sensed that the real interest was shifting subtly to another area while I was kept busy repeating myself.

Despite the initial good intent, the attainment of the designated goal of the study did not bring about a cordial reception of breathing coordination into medical practice. It was formally declared to be of great value in the management of emphysema and other pulmonary disorders involving dyspnea, but its introduction into practice assumed an importance secondary to the mounting interest in determining precisely what occurred within the respiratory mechanism and precisely how the occurrence was induced. For better or for worse, breathing coordination was being removed from the patient and into the realm of pure research. Although I was pleased with the opportunity to delve into cause and effect, the postponement of practical application was disappointing.

While the clouds were gathering above West Haven, the breathing coordination program at St. Albans was attracting the interest and attention which resulted in the demonstration for the Queens County Chapter of the National Tuberculosis Association. The metropolitan press had been invited by hospital authorities to the demonstration and had given it a gratifying amount of publicity. Through some confusion the *New York Times* was not represented at the demonstration. Shortly thereafter, a *Times* reporter called for a personal interview, which appeared in the paper the following Sunday. The interview mentioned that "The Stough Method of Breathing Coordination" was under investigation at the West Haven VA Hospital.

With the appearance of the *Times* story, the storm broke over West Haven. The pent-up antagonism arising from the

personality factor was unleashed, and I was sternly repri-
manded for personal self-seeking in the midst of scientific
research. Simultaneously, internal problems at the hospital
reached a crisis. The ensuing tumult threatened to inundate
the breathing coordination study. As a final touch to the snarl
of events, *The Reader's Digest* published its first general article
on emphysema, which at that time was an unpronounceable
word to the public and an enigma to the medical profession.
The work described in the article was counter that at West
Haven and gave small comfort in an area of serious distress.

In the wake of the *Times* interview came a flood of assorted
inquiries concerning the application and availability of breathing coordination. I had become accustomed to inquiries but
not in this number nor in such an extensive range of application. There were, of course, numerous emphysema sufferers
who sought relief. There were also many people with chronic
breathing problems who had tried everything and who were
grasping for any possible help. Some sought merely to improve
their health through an improvement of their breathing. The
numbers who wanted and needed to know more about their
breathing overwhelmed me. I could not have imagined that
so many knew so little about this most important of their
body's functions.

Along with the inquiries were a number of solid business
propositions from manufacturers of breathing machines and
devices to aid the breathing of emphysema patients and others
who suffered from respiratory disorders involving breathlessness. One letter stated candidly, "After all, you and I know
that they are all going to come back to the machines eventually." That struck me with forceful irony. The writer did not
know that breathing coordination gives the individual the
ability to manage his breathing without the use of machines

and devices. What impressed me even more was the realization that commercial interests hover like vultures above the suffering.

The availability of time limited the number of breathing coordination pupils accepted from among the inquirers. Those accepted for instruction were chosen for several reasons: the interest of their case histories, their particular need, their persistence in applying for instruction, their adaptability to my schedule. Some came hoping for a series of miracle exercises to solve their problems. Some came expecting sleight of hand to restore their damaged respiratory mechanism. Some were curiosity seekers. Others genuinely wanted help and were prepared to discipline themselves to obtain it. These last were the ones who could be taught breathing coordination and developed to the point of maintaining themselves independently.

While the crisis was under way in West Haven and inquiries were pouring into New York, St. Albans was having a staff changeover which drastically affected the work there. Although the development of breathing coordination represented a singular achievement, my sponsors had become thoroughly disillusioned by my failure to devise a teacher-training program and could no longer be interested in continuing either the medical study program or the hospital service program under any circumstances. The grant for both West Haven and St. Albans was terminating. When it expired, I would have to unearth new funds for any further exploration of breathing coordination.

For almost a year I had been working seven days a week trying to fulfill all the demands upon my time. I had believed that the documentation at St. Albans in combination with the study at West Haven would be sufficient to establish breathing coordination medically and that subsequent interest would provide the financial means for training medical personnel to teach breathing coordination in hospitals. I had been very sadly mistaken. My error brought me up shortly to a confrontation with myself.

St. Albans had been a service project with the research and study there a happy adjunct brought about by existing circumstances. When the circumstances no longer existed, further time at St. Albans would be a waste as far as the exploration of breathing coordination was concerned. West Haven, for all its turmoil, was otherwise. Dr. Nims had developed a heightened interest in breathing coordination when his work took him from the laboratory into the ward. As he came into direct contact with the patients, he could consider the effect of breathing coordination in human terms as well as scientific terms. His enthusiasm increased accordingly, and he proposed that we try to obtain funds to continue the study along different lines after the current grant expired.

Meanwhile, two emphysema sufferers who had been referred to me much earlier and who had arrested the progress of the disease with breathing coordination offered to help me if I should want to open an office to teach breathing coordination on a professional basis. Like Dr. Nims' proposal for continued research, their offer was unexpected. Because of certain restrictions of time, I could not accept both. I would have to choose, and in choosing I would determine the direction of my career.

The forces aligned for my battle with myself were formidable. I was physically tired. I was discouraged by delays and indifference. I had wearied of fighting lost causes. Despite all the advances made in breathing coordination, my hope of medical acceptance seemed no nearer fulfillment, and additional research appeared to be an exercise in futility for the satisfaction of curiosity. I was fast approaching the point at which curiosity became a luxury well beyond my means. On the other hand, a professional practice in management of breathing problems was almost an assured success. From the *Times* inquiries alone I could have set up a thriving practice and dispensed with the erratic schedules, loss of personal privacy, and unending demands on time and energy occasioned by research.

For several weeks the battle raged. One day I felt that I had put too much of my life into breathing coordination to abandon it. The next day I felt that I had put entirely enough of my life into breathing coordination and could not continue without some remuneration. Research certainly would bring me no financial reward. In fact, finances would have to be sought to continue it. Thinking strictly in terms of personal advantage, I could make only one choice—to open a professional office and go into the breathing business. Everyone told me I could make a fortune. I had no doubt that I could.

I wish I could say that I did not choose to open a professional office because of humanitarian considerations, that my awareness of breathing coordination's potential benefits to mankind prevented my capitulation to the temptations of finance. I wish I could, but I cannot. The honest truth of the matter is that I was too stubborn to let my ideas be turned aside by barriers of conventional thought. No amount of money would ever allay the frustration of failure to explore breathing coordination as completely as possible.

Thus the battle was fought. I did not know for some time whether I had won or lost.

8

THE COMMON FACTOR

Having filled a variety of roles in the serpentine course of my career, I decided in the winter of 1963 to turn super-sleuth. A mystery hung in the air and required, quite obviously, a bit of Sherlock Holmesing to undo it. Clues were in abundance, like a ring of keys with no lock to fit. The assignment, then, was to find the lock, fit the key, and discover whatever it was waiting to be discovered. I set about my latest role with cool objectivity.

For a long time before the work with the emphysema patients began at East Orange, I had been thinking about the curious similarity of effect that a particular manner of breathing had upon every temper and type of individual. The well and their breathing for maximum efficiency were my sole consideration in those days. I had observed in them a tendency to relax and breathe with greater ease and efficiency when a certain point in the instruction session had been reached. Although I could see it happening, I did not know why it happened nor did I have a formula for making it happen. Each pupil responded differently and required an individual approach.

My purpose was to teach the pupil to use all his muscles of

breathing in a unified pattern without calling upon one muscle or set of muscles to bear more of the workload of breathing than another. I instructed orally and suggested various maneuvers and attitudes to make the pupil aware of the muscular action. When I came to the ill and had to devise a new method of teaching, I had expected to achieve the same purpose, but I was not prepared to observe the same reaction. When it occurred, I concluded that a common factor existed not only among the well but also between the ill and the well.

As my method of teaching the ill evolved, I decided to apply it to the well to determine what effect, if any, it would have upon their breathing. The results caused me no little surprise. The point of relaxation was attained much more rapidly and breathing efficiency increased markedly. Of greater importance, I was able to detect unsuspected faults in the breathing mechanism and go about correcting them. Freedom from respiratory disease, I very quickly learned, did not necessarily mean freedom from respiratory faults.

No matter how widely divergent the physical condition of the individuals, a common factor existed in their manner of using their breathing mechanism. No two of them used the breathing mechanism in exactly the same way, yet the results were always parallel. Try as I would, I could not ferret out that common factor from among all the accumulating data.

Each new pupil, particularly one with an unusual case history, I regarded a possible lead to the answer. Perversely, new pupils seemed to serve only to deepen the mystery. When I was asked to undertake to aid the breathing of an eleven-year-old paralyzed from the neck down since the age of five as result of infection by an unknown virus, I hesitated because I was not sure I could help her. I knew I could not possibly harm her, but I was reluctant to raise her hope or that of her desperate parents, who had been consulting specialists here and abroad for six years. Her breathing was deteriorating at an alarming pace, however, and more satisfaction was to be gained from effort than from caution. This case was a very real challenge to all my knowledge and experience.

The child had no external sensations from the neck down. She could not so much as distinguish between hot and cold. She relied upon a respirator at night and during part of the day. In her breathing she used accessory muscles and gulped in air in a manner known as "frog breathing." To speak one complete sentence on a single breath lay beyond her respiratory ability.

Her personal charm and valiant effort diminished to inconsequence the difficulty of instruction. Within eight breathing coordination sessions, she developed a complete awareness of the coordinated pattern and could control it. Arrangements were made to take her to the West Haven laboratory for respiratory tests a month after instruction began then again three months later. In the interim she developed more nearly regular breathing and showed a significant increase in diaphragmatic excursion—in fact, a greater increase than that achieved with the electrical stimulus of specialized breathing apparatus. Her comprehension and discipline were such that in time she became able to maintain herself independently for periods as long as thirty-six hours. With this achievement she could fly to Rome with her family for a summer holiday on the Mediterranean.

Her progress pleased me immensely. It also perplexed me. Where did she, a severely handicapped child, fit into the pattern? I did not know, yet I had observed and documented with her the same remarkable effects breathing coordination produced in everyone else. Long discussions with Dr. Nims and others gave me a keener insight into her respiratory condition and her many physical problems, but they did not explain the similarity of effects of breathing coordination. There had to be an answer somewhere.

After the grant for St. Albans and the initial West Haven studies had expired, additional funds became available for further probing into the nature and potentials of breathing coordination. Dr. Nims as medical supervisor was especially interested in breaking down my method of instruction into its components to determine precisely what I did in establishing breathing coordination. He felt that such an analysis would facilitate the development of an instruction formula for the medical profession and would serve to explain breathing coordination. Although I did not share his viewpoint, the line of investigation proposed would leave me free to sort and study data and try to answer the questions which nagged at my mind.

Before any new areas were explored at West Haven, the St. Albans findings were reviewed, verified, and documented by Dr. Ledwith for medical presentation. At last all the necessary charts and graphs were available to prove that what the patients said was happening and what any observer could plainly see was happening had happened indeed. St. Albans had documented the effect of breathing coordination on various segments of the respiratory mechanism but not on the total mechanism. In the West Haven laboratory, pneumographs and roentgen-kymographs were employed to document the synergism resulting from breathing coordination. A weakness in any area was clearly indicated by alteration of another. The prior work and theories stood up beneath the scrutiny of the latest techniques and devices for measuring change in respiratory condition.

While the consolidation of the ramified breathing coordination findings was in progress, another opportunity arose to test the flexibility of application of breathing coordination to respiratory problems. Much to the bewilderment of the West Haven VA Hospital staff, a former service nurse applied for admission to the emphysema ward. She had learned of the work in breathing coordination and had promptly set about arranging her infiltration of this traditionally male domain. When the shock of having a woman about the place had worn off, the men on the ward were rather pleased with the novelty of the situation. Her case was not especially novel of itself but subsequent developments were.

A heavy smoker in her early forties, she had contracted a serious respiratory infection which left extensive lung damage. She was not aware of any respiratory difficulty until she experienced a rather sudden loss of breath and found that she could no longer sustain her customary activities. She was diagnosed as having advanced emphysema. When she entered the hospital, she was gasping for breath and was never comfortable in any position. She could not walk nor could she speak a complete sentence. Her use of accessory muscles for breathing was further complicated by the contraction of the upper abdomen on the inhale.

Within five breathing coordination sessions she changed completely to a coordinated pattern and could breathe freely. A throat congestion cleared, the voice improved, and she was able to walk about a hundred feet and take care of her personal grooming. Before she had time for the muscles of breathing to develop sufficiently to sustain her increased activity, she left the hospital because of personal matters. Her private situation was such that the tensions produced by it aggravated the existing respiratory condition of emphysema. Over a relatively short while she had a series of secondary illnesses which put her in a critical condition.

Her return to the hospital, which she had left too soon, was almost too late. This trip was by ambulance and with the administration of oxygen. She had not eaten in days, and when she arrived, she was more nearly dead than alive. She had lapsed into unconsciousness, her respiratory rate was dangerously low, and she was not responding to medication. The hospital staff was at an impasse because administration of additional oxygen could cause suffocation and use of the iron lung standing ready outside her room could shock her into a heart attack.

Since she had not developed her respiratory muscles as fully as she might have, the illnesses had altered her breathing, and her latter state was worse than the first. Midafternoon I began working with her, using palpation and light massage to keep the abdominal muscle and the pectorals relaxed in order to reestablish her breathing coordination. Although she was only semi-conscious at times, her earlier training enabled her to respond. She was being fed intravenously all the while. For five hours, under the observation of doctors who were powerless to help, she lay between life and death. When her respiration faltered, I was able to stimulate it with a light touch and keep the respiratory mechanism functioning in her pattern of breathing coordination.

Late in the evening after she had passed the crisis and was breathing in her coordinated pattern, quietly, unaided, I went home to think. What was the common factor between a dying woman in a Connecticut hospital and every other person I had taught, sick or well? What was there in breathing coordination that it functioned effectively even when the user was unconscious? Still, I had no answer. I had witnessed the happening as I participated in it, but I could not explain it.

A week later the patient was off the critical list. In two weeks she had recovered, and in a month she was walking. Her experience that desperate afternoon left me with the feeling that somehow I had come a step closer to an answer. I had seen something I should have recognized but had not because I was expecting something else.

So far, my super-sleuthing had added up to a lot of suspicions but no real evidence. Practical laboratory work, however, turned up a quantity of valuable material. To eliminate the subjective element and make the evaluation of the emphysema patient's condition wholly objective, the treadmill was employed. This test measured the length of time the patient could remain on a treadmill and the amount of energy he burned when he breathed oxygen and when he used breathing coordination without oxygen. The results with breathing coordination proved superior to those with oxygen. With breathing coordination the patient could tell the moment he had reached his maximum exertion, stop before he went into accessory breathing, and thereby avoid dyspnea and panic. With oxygen he had a false sense of capability and overexerted before he was aware of what he had done. He then went into accessory breathing and on to exhaustion and difficult recovery.

Further tests involved spirometry to measure forced breathing against breathing coordination. Here, too, the results were better with breathing coordination, because the respiratory mechanism always responds more efficiently in a state of relaxed effort than in a state of tension, as is induced by forced breathing. Another new element introduced into the study was the voice tape to document the changes in the voice as breathing coordination developed. Such changes had been observed previously but had never been documented. The tapes strikingly illustrated the changes in voice timbre and degree of intensity. They also showed the increase in ability to sustain speech and the elimination of coughs, throat clearing, and various conditions which had gone unattended. No longer was reliance on observation alone necessary. Here was proof recorded.

The stockpiling of documentation should have cheered me and it did, but not as much as it might have if I had not kept wondering how all these things fit together. I could not escape the feeling that I was staring at something quite obvious but to which, for some reason or other, I was completely blind. I had often been bitterly frustrated in my discussions with doctors when I realized that their mental bent and medical indoctrination made impossible their comprehension of certain aspects of breathing coordination. I remember well the doctor who stood up after a fully-documented lecture-demonstration and commented, "This has been most interesting, but, of course, we all know that once the chest has been raised, the lower, more normal position cannot again be established." What he had witnessed had not penetrated his original convictions. He could not believe in anything contrary to what he had once learned and accepted as final authority. His purblindness was exceeded only by my own as my mind kept traveling round and round breathing coordination, failing to identify anything I did not know already from experience or inference.

Into this interim of intensive study and exploration wandered another desperate individual with an unusual problem. He came not long after the introduction of the voice tapes, and the nature of his problem was such that I decided to have a go at it despite an overcrowded schedule.

The young man, then in his late teens, had a speech impediment which threatened the whole structure of his adult life and forebode even more complicated psychological problems than he had already experienced. The impediment had not appeared until the latter part of childhood, but it had become steadily worse as he grew older. Although I ordinarily would not suggest breathing coordination as a panacea for speech defects, the circumstances of his case persuaded me that it might help him.

When he was not quite ten years old, he had almost drowned in a public swimming pool. The children were playing noisily and the lifeguard was inattentive. By the time the boy was missed, his body had submerged and a pulmotor was required to revive him. After a week in an oxygen tent and nearly a month in the hospital, he went home for a recuperative period of a week or so before going back to school. His parents were so thankful for his survival that they were not unduly concerned by the slight stammer in his speech. His condition was thought to be nothing more than a natural nervous reaction to a harrowing experience which he would outgrow eventually. Meanwhile, he attended speech classes in school to help him overcome his difficulty.

Instead of disappearing, the stammer became steadily worse. The boy received special instruction, but that did not improve his speech. One doctor who was consulted in the case attributed the problem to shock and recommended private school. When private school failed to solve the problem, speech and voice therapy had a turn but produced no lasting benefits. Over the years the deterioration of the boy's speech affected his schoolwork so severely that he was not expected to be graduated from high school. He was rejected for military service because of his inability to repeat commands, and his social contacts narrowed almost to nothingness as communication became increasingly more painful for him to attempt.

Since the condition had arisen from an accident involving the respiratory mechanism, I suspected that damage to the mechanism might be the cause of inability to sustain speech. I knew what I was looking for and I found it almost immediately. When the young man spoke, the abdomen protruded. From the work in emphysema I had learned that the protrusion of the abdomen in the effort of speech is the sure sign of a weakened diaphragm. A weakened diaphragm cannot support the air pressure required for speech but will invert, causing pressure in the lower abdomen and the subsequent protrusion.

Too much damage had been incurred over too long a time for the speech fault to be eliminated entirely, but the improvement was great. With the redevelopment of the diaphragmatic muscle through breathing coordination, the young man learned to manage his breathing well enough to maintain himself under conditions of stress and prevent the former incoherencies of his speech. He could then go about his life in a normal manner.

After my experience with the young man, I returned, somewhat the wiser, to my pursuit of the common factor in breathing which I believed to exist among all people regardless of physical condition. Because I knew what I was looking for in the case of the young man, I was able to succeed where others had failed. What, I asked myself, was I looking for now? Essentially, I was in search of a norm, a "correct" pattern of breathing against which I could measure the progress and development of my pupils. They all had to be doing something right, or the results of their breathing coordination could not have paralleled. They could not all have had the same relaxation and release of tension, the same muscular development, the same voice improvement, if something were not the same among them all.

I pondered. I probed. I puzzled. I pored over everything at my disposal. I prayed for insight into the mysteries of breathing. Leisurely, like a cloud shaping on the horizon, an idea began to take form in my mind. Indistinct at first, it separated itself gradually from the accumulated mass of thought on the subject of breathing and breathing coordination. The edges rounded out and, slowly, it drifted free to stand alone in monumental grandeur. Its utter, beautiful simplicity astonished me. What astonished me even more was the realization that my common factor had been lying in plain view all the time. It was so obvious that I, in expectation of the recondite, had failed repeatedly to notice it.

After all the years, there it was, my long-sought common factor: nothing other than breathing coordination itself!

When I had recovered from the unique experience of discovery, I was able to identify the error in my thought which had obscured the obvious for so long a time. Since the results were identical, I had expected the cause to be identical. I was looking for something with no variation from individual to individual. The variances had deceived me. In spite of my constant awareness of individual differences, I had fallen into the trap of thinking conventionally that everything can be reduced to a convenient formula. Nothing could be more highly individualistic than the manner in which a person breathes to fulfill the unique requirements of his body at a given moment.

Breathing coordination is *the* correct pattern for a particular individual, not a general pattern which can be applied to every individual.

107

To verify the discovery, Dr. Nims and I worked through the data step by step countless times, always with the same conclusion. In early 1964 we were able to state unequivocally that there is no absolute "correct" method of breathing; there is only breathing coordination. The muscles and sets of muscles of the human respiratory mechanism are designed to operate in a perfectly coordinated synergism to give the individual the maximum breathing efficiency of which he is capable and to give it to him with a minimum expenditure of energy.

Regardless of respiratory handicap or damage, the mechanism can be trained to function in a coordinated pattern with the work load of breathing evenly distributed over the operable portions of the mechanism. Each person, according to his physical structure, has his own individualistic pattern of breathing for maximum efficiency with minimum effort. If he suffers any form of respiratory damage, his muscles can be retrained to compensate the disability without overuse of any single muscle or sets of muscles. Breathing coordination can exist under any respiratory condition.

Slowly, my mind encompassed and digested the staggering realization. All the years—then some sixteen or so since I had begun to look for a common factor—all those years of thought and experiment and development had been climaxing before my very eyes and I had not seen because I had been in search of something else. A new continent had been reached, and I had thought I was coming round to the Indies.

Contrary to my previous notions, breathing coordination was not the name of something I did. It was a physiological fact, heretofore unknown, which I had discovered in my efforts to help emphysema patients breathe more easily. Breathing coordination is the intended function of the respiratory system just as digestion is the intended function of the digestive system.

Unfortunately, the discovery of breathing coordination was complicated by the attempt to explain my method of establishing it. The Stough Method of Breathing Coordination was taken as an entity rather than as components. Breathing coordination is. It exists. It existed before I discovered it and will continue to exist long after I cease to practice The Stough Method. The Stough Method is what I do to cause the muscles to function in the originally intended pattern of breathing coordination. The method is the instruction technique I use to establish breathing coordination. Others may develop other methods. Methods will change, but breathing coordination will remain.

My long, sometimes discouraging, always exciting search was ended. Now came the arduous task of making the findings known.

9

A NEW DIRECTION

Before the formal medical presentation of the work in breathing coordination could be made, a considerable amount of research remained to be done. Like it or not, I had to accept that fact. So I did, but not very gracefully. I was not a doctor, nor was I under any direct obligation to the medical profession. I chafed against the pedantry which delayed the progress of the investigations into the many applications of breathing coordination. Medical acceptance of my discovery of a new physiological fact would have slight effect upon my career other than to eliminate a certain degree of skepticism. On the other hand, the new physiological fact would be of immense benefit in the practice of medicine. I could not bring myself to stand about and wait patiently for all the formalities of presentation, deliberation, and acceptance to be fulfilled.

While Dr. Nims continued his analysis of The Stough Method for inclusion in the medical report on the work in breathing coordination, I advised major figures in the respiratory field in this country and abroad of the discovery. A series of informal reports detailing study procedure and documenting results served to bridge the anticipated gap between the conclusion of the research and the publication of the report on the

111

work. The response to these initial communications was gratifyingly cordial.

Preparation of the medical material proceeded at what for me rivaled the pace of a lame snail. The complications were legion because of the radical nature of the subject. In the year 1964 there were areas of conventional thought which made the scholasticism of the Middle Ages seem avant-garde, and into these areas had to be introduced ideas completely counter accepted concepts. So little creative thought had been applied to the process of breathing that few were aware of the poverty of knowledge of the subject. Error had been laid upon error and passed on as fact.

Although I had not the least desire to clash with standard teaching, breathing coordination was hurtling me headlong into conflict. First of all, my lay status generated prejudice. That anyone other than a medical man could think of anything in the realm of physiological functions was past comprehension for some. To compound the difficulty, the conventional terminology of the respiratory field carried with it overtones and implications which misled and confused in the consideration of a new subject. Here were two obstacles to surmount before approaching the heart of the matter and boldly setting forth ideas counter the conventional. Two of the startling achievements of breathing coordination were the development of involuntary muscles and the alteration of chest position, both of which had been considered impossible. In numerous instances, visible proof had failed to dismiss skepticism.

At this juncture in my career, I had been a laborer in the field of medicine for six years, four of which had been spent in intensive formal research and all of which had been under constant medical scrutiny and advisement. I had instructed hundreds of people of varying degrees of respiratory disability, and I had learned more about human beings and the way they breathe than I would ever have imagined possible six years earlier. Repeatedly, the results had been tested and confirmed.

From my six years in hospitals and my prior experience and experiments in the field of breathing, I had come to a deepening realization of the profound effect of the act of breathing on the total human being. I had also learned, with mounting distress, how very little is known of the manifold effects of the act of breathing on the several systems of the body and how very little attention is paid the respiratory system until it is damaged. The need for broader knowledge of breathing is great among medical men and the public alike. The need for research into the ramifications of the act of breathing is even greater.

Knowing that breathing coordination is an immediate aid in respiratory problems and a potential aid in numerous other areas of human disorder, I became more and more impatient with the niggling over The Stough Method. Here was a whole new world to explore, and attention focused not upon it but upon the means used to get to it. I had the smothering sensation that breathing coordination could be buried forever beneath sheaves of medical papers. Some sort of conclusive action had to be taken to forestall that possibility.

While the medical work went on leisurely, I began to cast about for ways of extending investigations into the applications of breathing coordination and of disseminating the ideas already gleaned. My several interests were now concentrated in breathing coordination, and I wanted some vehicle to convey them all. I wanted to put myself in a position not only to conduct research and explore the field of breathing further but also to stimulate thought in the area of breathing, to instruct, and to make breathing coordination available on as extensive a basis as possible. The more I thought, the keener became my realization that I could not accomplish my purpose alone. I needed a great deal of help.

Setting up a professional office and hiring a staff was an obvious answer to my need, but to me it seemed inappropriate. A professional office smacked too much of commerce, a possibility which I had already dismissed as incompatible with my basic interests. What was required was some sort of organization to embody and perpetuate the idea of breathing coordination, an organization that could grow and make a significant contribution in the field of breathing.

After a period of deliberation and consultation I concluded that my purposes could be served best by the founding of an institute for research and education in the field of breathing. Such an institute would have to have a name, of course, and like everything else in my life, that name would have to encompass multiple considerations. It would have to single out breathing coordination from among the other schools and practices of breathing. Further, it would have to distinguish The Stough Method of Breathing Coordination from other methods of teaching breathing coordination, which conceivably may be developed in time, and from other methods of teaching other forms of breathing.

Once again, to protect important considerations, the final resort was the odious introduction of personality into what might have remained to advantage an impersonal area. The newly-found institute was dubbed The Carl Stough Institute of Breathing Coordination and duly incorporated. The incorporation proceedings came about with the aid and advice of breathing coordination pupils and persons interested in breathing coordination.

114

Regardless of the nobility of purpose served, long names are like elephants in traffic; they impede the movement of a high-speed civilization. The long name of the new organization had to be changed to something more wieldy. For practical use, therefore, it was neatly trimmed to The Stough Institute. The same held true for The Stough Method of Breathing Coordination. That was reduced to initials, SMBC, and transformed into phonetics as SIMBIC. Operations could now proceed without undue delays arising from tongue-twisters.

Officers and advisers of the Institute were either pupils or associates in breathing coordination. The principal officers were emphysema sufferers in whom breathing coordination had arrested the progress of the disease. Because breathing coordination had been discovered in the search for relief of the dyspnea of emphysema, early interest in the Institute tended to concentrate in the application of SIMBIC to that disease. Work at both St. Albans and West Haven and in my private instruction alone had indicated that SIMBIC had far more uses. However, before I went into formal investigations of the numerous applications of SIMBIC, I decided to indulge myself a bit and satisfy a curiosity I had entertained for a long time.

As early as East Orange I had had among the advanced emphysema patients former athletes of varying degrees of proficiency. Because of their basic muscular coordination which enabled them to excel in athletics, they usually were easier to instruct and quicker to learn than most of the others. Working with them, I often wondered about the breathing patterns and habits of first-rate athletes in prime condition. I fancied that some of them might have retained into adulthood the natural breathing coordination with which most people are born but tend to lose in infancy and childhood. I had seen the worst of respiratory conditions and I wanted to round out my experience with the best.

The files of the new Institute were filled with case histories of respiratory disease and disorder and with accounts of the effects of SIMBIC upon the well—that is, persons free of respiratory complaints. For purposes of comparative study, data on the respiratory condition of the physically superior would be highly worthwhile. As administrator of the Institute, I proposed that the initial project be an investigation of the respiratory condition and breathing habits of athletes. I was eager to take a new direction in my thoughts and in my activities. Happily, I set out on the path which led me to the United States Olympic Committee, through the Boys' Club of New York, and on to Coach Giegengack of Yale, to whom I had to prove the increase in respiratory efficiency brought about by SIMBIC. By the time I had reached Yale, I was a few years older and wiser and perhaps a little less impatient, but I still chafed against the ever-present necessity of endlessly proving the effectiveness of SIMBIC.

Despite the relative brevity of the Yale project, so little time remained until the Olympic High Altitude Medical Testing and Study Program at South Lake Tahoe, California, that the weeks seemed eternal. The Yale men developed steadily and showed all the side benefits of SIMBIC, but Gieg remained enigmatic. When openings in the schedule permitted Gieg and Bill Dayton, his trainer, to have SIMBIC instruction and to experience for themselves the effects, their interest and enthusiasm increased. Still, I had no inkling of Gieg's thoughts on the proposal to incorporate SIMBIC into the regimen of the Olympic candidates as a health and safety measure, quite apart from the probability of improved performance. If he were not convinced of the value of SIMBIC to his men, no chance existed that the other Olympic coaches ever would be.

After an agonizing stretch of time, I learned in a very casual manner that something of significance had occurred. Since trackmen for the most part are self-contained and not given to talk about their accomplishments, I rarely had any information from the runners themselves about their personal performances. The report was almost certain to come from someone else. In this instance, all that I could find out immediately was that some personal performance records had been broken. That gave me hope to go on.

Later, when I received my copy of Gieg's report to Dr. Stiles of the Olympic Medical and Training Services Committee, I read: "After eight breathing coordination sessions and all together on the same date all four of my men produced their best lifetime performances. I would like to think it was my training methods but it is too dramatic to call it coincidence, especially since men who were not put through this routine did not show such dramatic improvement." In another communication with Dr. Stiles, Gieg further attested: "In the case of my own men, our recovery time has been halved. Men now effectively double in twenty-five minutes who usually needed fifty." Whatever I had anticipated, this was even more.

Gieg was very deliberate in his decisions, but when he had made up his mind, he proceeded with hurricane force and monumental determination. During his enigmatic period his mind must have been clicking away like a calculator, totaling all the factors involved in the inclusion of SIMBIC in the 1968 Olympic program. I was certain that one of the most impressive factors was not the performance record but the reduction in recovery time, for Gieg had an uncommon concern for the health and safety of his men. Convinced that SIMBIC would be of advantage to the U.S. Olympic candidates, he immediately put into motion the complicated machinery required to persuade the other Olympic coaches that SIMBIC would be a good thing. He himself had been persuaded both by his personal experience and by the experience of his trackmen. He would have undertaken the removal of mountains if the removal of mountains had been required.

Unfortunately, the effects of SIMBIC always sounded too good to be true, because the requisite to the achievement of those effects was seldom taken into consideration. At the mention of breathing, most tend to think of a given series of calisthenics of one sort or another to bring about an improvement in respiratory function. Before SIMBIC can be understood, that concept has to be dismissed entirely. SIMBIC is not a magic formula for good breathing. It is a carefully disciplined process of retraining the muscles of respiration to operate in a synergistic pattern for peak efficiency with minimum effort. Once the discipline is achieved and the respiratory muscles have developed sufficiently, the benefits are innumerable. The too-good-to-be-true effects begin to appear only after the initial conditions have been fulfilled.

In presenting SIMBIC to the Olympic coaches, who had no prior knowledge of it nor any reason to think it other than another variety of breathing measure, Gieg ran into a mountain of skepticism. He was equal to the challenge. He wrote letters and the Institute supplied reports on athletic and other investigations preceding the Yale project. Our combined mailings that spring were considerable. Convincing people at hand is difficult enough; convincing them long distance is a herculean task. But, Gieg had espoused SIMBIC, and long after I had run out of answers, he still had a few left.

Accustomed as I was to waiting for decisions, I knew I could not afford the luxury of indolence while the course of the future was determined. I had to assume the positive and be prepared for it; otherwise, I could not act upon it with the speed the waning time demanded. If I got a negative, I would have time in abundance to plot my next course of investigation of the respiratory conditions and habits of athletes.

With the accrual of the beneficial results of SIMBIC to the Yale trackmen, word of the breathing project circulated through the Athletic Department, and an opportunity arose to work with the swimming team. It proved to be the perfect solution to the immediate problem of preparing for the future. It also gave me a chance to check on the respiratory status of swimmers and observe their response to SIMBIC.

Gieg and I had discussed the probable conditions which would exist at South Lake Tahoe during the Olympic high altitude program. In all likelihood my schedule would call for SIMBIC instruction for some eighty athletes a week. Each athlete would require an individual session, because breathing coordination can be taught only on an individual basis. I had never undertaken so extensive a teaching project in so limited an amount of time. I was not at all sure how I should go about it.

The Yale swimming team entered the scene at precisely the right moment. The track team was going to be away at the time the swimming team was readying for competition. I could work with the swimmers while the trackmen did not need me. Since the period of SIMBIC instruction was to be limited, I would be able to determine how rapidly I could handle individual sessions, how rapidly the athlete could assimilate instructions, and at what pace physical development might be expected under such circumstances. All of this information was vital to the planning of an instruction program for the Olympic candidates.

The swimmers benefited from their accelerated course and so did I. I learned much about the respiratory condition and habits of swimmers and accumulated an amount of data for Institute purposes. Most important, I found out what I needed to know in order to draw up an instruction program plan for South Lake Tahoe. However, I failed to discover among the swimmers what I always hope to find in working with persons in superior physical condition—someone with perfect breathing coordination and without respiratory faults.

When the track team returned to New Haven with fresh triumphs, I had the instruction program pretty well formulated. Gieg and I worked out the details while we waited for the response of the coaches to the proposed SIMBIC project. Since the project was a cooperative undertaking to be sponsored jointly on a mutual interest basis by The Stough Institute and the United States Olympic Committee, conceivably it could proceed without the approval of the coaches, but then the full burden of sponsorship would fall on the Institute. Furthermore, the extent of success under those conditions would be highly questionable.

I needed the approval and the cooperation of the coaches to accomplish all that I hoped to accomplish for the Institute and for the Olympic Committee. Few athletes were likely to take an interest in any measure their coaches did not endorse. Regardless of my convictions or desires, I could not teach anyone who did not want to be taught. Nor could I find out a great deal about the respiratory condition of anyone who would not work with me. Two years or so of preparatory study and planning, not to mention a sizable portion of Institute funds, had gone into the Olympic program. Not to be able to fulfill it satisfactorily would be extremely disappointing.

Mail sped back and forth across the country as I busied myself in practice of the virtue of patience. I was not without other preoccupations in the interim, fortunately, but none of them seemed to be of sufficient magnitude to block out my concern for the Olympic program. I could understand the reservations in appraising something new by long distance, but my understanding failed to bring me any consolation. The thought of being so near yet so far from realization of a great effort and a great desire created almost unbearable tension.

Many times when I have been in tense situations—and those times have been numerous—I have known that without my own development and practice of breathing coordination to dissipate the tensions, I should long ago have fallen victim to ulcers, heart disease, and all the other attendant evils of life in a progressive civilization. If for no other reason than self-preservation, I consider all the years of research well worth the effort.

During the crisis of the coaches, breathing coordination served me admirably. My nerves stretched and frayed, but they did not quite snap. Each day I told myself in utter seriousness what I frequently told my pupils and patients in jest: "Keep breathing!" I did, as the hours agonizingly spun out into eons.

10

METAMORPHOSIS

On the whole, Olympic coaches are not prone to snap judgments. They approached SIMBIC with abundant caution and weighed me in the balance with great care. I was no stranger to the judgment scales, but I had never found them particularly comfortable for protracted periods. I wondered why I permitted myself to climb into them so readily.

I could have done other gainful things with my life than deal in the vagaries of breathing. At least, I like to think I could have, but I am not entirely certain. The metamorphosis was so subtle that no line could be drawn at any single point in my life to divide one interest, one career, from another. Each derived from the other and complemented the other.

Breathing, whether an area for scientific research or for instruction in practical application to the production of sound, is admittedly a rather unusual subject with which to become involved. It leads to no end of tedious, albeit well-intended jokes which automatically stifle the development of further conversation along that line. Occasionally it does elicit challenging questions with answers too personal or too involved to make. Every now and again it will generate a query that lingers in my mind long after and compels me to consider it in a different light.

Persons who are familiar with my work in the medical field and who are disconcerted by my lack of a medical degree are wont to ask such questions. One that is directed to me with almost predictable regularity is, "If you're not a doctor, how did you get into breathing, anyway?"

Oddly, the comprehensive reply is not a forthright account of the events leading to my entry into the medical field. After much thought, I have concluded that the answer should run more like this: "If I were a medical doctor, I should not be in the field of breathing at all. My studies and orientation would have faced me in another direction. I would be, instead, in the respiratory field treating respiratory diseases and disorders. If I had been absorbed in the treatment of respiratory disease or in the several functions of the respiratory system, I would never have discovered breathing coordination."

I came into the field of breathing through the only door open to me. I came by way of sound. Until I worked with the emphysema patients in East Orange, my thoughts on breathing were always in terms of the production of sound, primarily the sound of the human voice. I had observed certain psychological and physiological effects of breathing in a given fashion, but my chief concern was the sound resulting from that fashion of breathing. My ear was acute, and I could detect the moment the breathing had gone wrong and changed the sound.

At East Orange my preoccupation with the sound of the voices of the emphysema patients prodded me to the realization that the ability to sustain sound was in direct correlation with the ability to exert physical effort. From that point I reasoned that the air required to produce sound of a given length and quality would serve as a self-regulating graded force against which the muscles employed in the exhale could work and develop. If I had been a medical doctor, I should have reasoned solely in terms of forced movement of volumes of air in and out the lungs, for that would have been all that concerned me. Yet, unregulated and ungraded force on the exhale can damage muscles already weakened and ultimately do more harm than good.

Awareness of the quality of the voice in sustaining sound further drew my attention to the protrusion of the abdomen on the exhale as an indication of diaphragmatic weakness and inversion under pressure. If I had been a medical doctor, I would have been occupied wholly with the principal muscles of breathing and the function of the respiratory system entire. In all probability the abdominal protrusion would have seemed of small significance, and certainly it would not have been related to the accompanying tension in the upper chest area. I was accustomed to suspecting an error in the breathing when the sound of the voice altered and to inventing ways of eliminating the error.

Sound was one of my most reliable guides through the maze of respiratory complications. Before I ever began working with a pupil or patient, I could determine his general physical condition by the sound of his voice. The respiratory system is the balance wheel of the body, and sound is the gauge of the respiratory system. When the breathing is aberrant, the body is affected. Conversely, something amiss in the body will affect the breathing. The same, of course, is true of psychological pressures as well as physical.

The whole reason for my being consulted and brought into the medical work at East Orange in 1958 was that I had then developed an effective method for teaching the well how to breathe with increased efficiency for the production of sound.

Sound, at that point, did not enter the medical scene, but the increased efficiency of breathing did. I had been dealing with various problems of breathing among the well for a number of years and had evolved an instruction technique for correcting flaws in the breathing pattern and for using the breathing mechanism with a higher degree of efficiency than had been possible previously. An important element of my technique was the use of sound to detect and correct errors in breathing. My acute physical sense of hearing was augmented by a mental quirk which enabled me to hear sound not only as it was actually but as it should be. When I listened to a voice, I did not hear the voice alone. I heard also the voice as it should be, properly developed, and I generally knew almost immediately what was wrong with it and how to correct it.

For me, the voice was not an entity that required breath for its activation and embellishment. The voice was the breath acting upon tissues and passages of the body to produce sound. The sound so produced bore a direct relationship to the effective function of the respiratory system. The sound could not be correct unless the breathing were correct.

Just when in my life I became intrigued by the sound of the human voice, I could not say. As a child I had a pleasing voice and ample opportunity to use it. Possibly, fascination with my own voice was the beginning. At any rate, my voice, my keen aural sense, and an amount of musical talent eventually precipitated my enrollment in Westminster Choir College, Princeton, New Jersey, in the mid-1940's. There I sang with Westminster Choir and worked with the late Dr. John Finley Williamson, whose passion for choral tone, achieved by the development of individual singers to professional soloist abilities, made a deep impression on me. Dr. Williamson also made me aware of the effect of my breathing on the sound of my voice. From that awareness grew my interest in the intricate relationship between breathing and the sound of the voice.

A question sometimes put to me by former classmates is, "What do you know that we don't know?" The logical implication is: "After all, we attended the same classes, heard the same lectures, read the same books. How could you have found in those sources something we missed?"

I have learned to dismiss such questions with a light remark, for answering becomes too tedious to be worthwhile. As so logically implied, what I received from the classroom *was* basically the same. I was not an assiduous student. With only the least effort, anyone could have acquired a great deal more general knowledge than I did from formal schooling. The difference lay in my attitude toward the sound of the voice.

For me the classroom was primarily a training ground, a place in which I was taught the routine concepts and procedures followed in the choral profession. I did not really begin to learn until I tested those concepts and procedures in an actual situation. Even as a student I had a chance to do that by filling the post of weekend choir director in nearby Trenton and Philadelphia churches. What was of no value to me I quickly discarded. What I could use I explored and elaborated upon and shaped to suit my particular need. I was constantly trying to match the choral tone I actually heard with my ear to the tone sounding insistently in my mind.

The choirs I worked with were made up of volunteers, most of whom were vocally and musically untrained. I realized very quickly that I had set an impossible goal for myself, that I would do well even to approach the desired choral tone. If I wanted to hear the ideal sound, I would have to find some way of producing it from the voices at my disposal. To that end, I gave private voice lessons to the choir members and had the satisfaction of hearing unmistakable improvement in the choral tone.

Graduation came none too soon for me. I was eager to be off and away in pursuit of my several theories of creating plural tone with individual voices. Again my master plan was to take each voice, analyze it, and proceed to develop it toward its highest potential. I believed that voices so developed and trained to sing together would be like an orchestra, each instrument at its best attuned to the others. Such a group should produce a choral tone of surpassing virility and beauty.

Of the job opportunities open to me after graduation, the one that seemed most likely to permit me the freedom to test my ideas was the First Presbyterian Church in Rocky Mount, North Carolina. The church had no choir program and would be happy with anything I could do to provide one. The choir was composed of considerably less than a dozen members, but, I told myself cheerfully, that could be remedied. The remedy required several foot-tours of the business district to persuade the men of the church to have a try at the choir. The ladies of the church were somewhat more musically inclined.

During my years at Westminster I had experimented enough with my own voice and breathing to believe that only defects of the throat or ear prevented singing. To build my new choir, I announced with infinite calm that I positively would teach anyone to sing who did not have a limiting physical defect. Service in the choir was the only other requisite to free instruction. The challenge was designed to stir up the spirit of the young and lighthearted. It did, and a few weeks and scores of voice lessons later the church had a choir of some thirty enthusiastic members.

At that time I had not entirely given up the idea of a career in voice, and I continued to explore the possibilities of my own voice while I was teaching my new choir members, many of them not only voice but the fundamentals of music as well. As I worked on my own problems of breathing for the production of sound, I could observe the same problems in the people I taught. Both in myself and in others I found that emotion produced a breath-restricting tension and altered the sound. I invented various physical maneuvers to eliminate the tension and free the breathing. Always, when the breathing fell into an unrestricted pattern, the pupil relaxed and could begin to achieve his voice potential.

With this system of individual teaching augmenting the overall choir instruction and rehearsal, I came even nearer to the choral tone which was persistently in my mind. The excitement of watching the choir grow and hearing the voices change stimulated the community. That Christmas I was able to put together a community choral group for the presentation of the first part of Handel's *Messiah*. In the late 1940's, such a presentation was a stellar achievement. From the success of the Christmas performance grew the idea of a community choral group for those who enjoyed choral singing and who were willing to make the usual bargain with me—voice lessons in exchange for faithful group membership. Eventually, the membership was stabilized at forty.

My theory of training voices individually and combining them to achieve a superior choral instrument with a unique tone was realized in both the church choir and the community choral group. News of the group's exceptional ability spread abroad rapidly, and in the first season we were invited to replace the Westminster Choir in special performance of Paul Green's outdoor music drama, *The Lost Colony*, in Manteo,

129

North Carolina. That was the era of the Robert Shaw Chorale and other such personalized choral organizations; so, my group quite naturally became the Carl Stough Chorale.

The four years I spent in Rocky Mount were filled with all the high excitement and adventure of youthful testings. I was practically unrestricted and could experiment to my heart's content with tone and breathing and the production of sound. Somewhere in among those years I began to realize that I did not have the true musician's approach to choral work. Although I selected the best of choral repertoire for both the church choir and the Chorale, I was not the least interested in the exploration of recondite works and the presentation of elaborate choral programs. My interest lay, rather, in the total choral sound produced in the combination of voices individually trained to their greatest potential. The absorption with sound brought me back to the development of the individual voice, which took me even farther back to breathing as the basis for the correct production of sound. My interest in music did not match my interest in the sound of the human voice and the influence of breathing upon it.

The Chorale achieved an extraordinary tone which was appreciated if not perceived by those who heard it. The group enjoyed a considerable degree of renown in the Upper South and toured as extensively as was then possible for amateur singers with jobs to consider. We had a return engagement with *The Lost Colony*, an appearance at the Mosque in Richmond, Virginia, other appearances around North Carolina, and concerts and oratorio performances in Rocky Mount. The crowning accomplishment was a season of a half-hour sustaining broadcast on Sunday evening over the now-defunct Liberty national network.

The success of the Liberty broadcasts drew the attention of

other networks, and I was soon in a position to take a chance on organizing a professional group in New York to present a similar series. The temptation was too much for me, particularly when it was accompanied by the opportunity to study voice with the late Paul Althouse. One hot Sunday morning in mid-August of 1953 I got married and set out that afternoon for New York City.

Totally innocent of the vicissitudes of the fair island of Manhattan, I arrived upon its shores with an abundance of plans and projects and promises and a glaring insufficiency of wherewithal. I began work immediately with Mr. Althouse. His dynamic approach to teaching so intrigued me that the other events of the time appeared far less formidable than they actually were. Under his tutelage I was freed of my tendency to analyze myself constantly, and I began again to have thoughts of a concert career.

Simultaneously, I was conferring with radio and television network officials and potential sponsors about an elaboration of the Chorale's Liberty series for the following season. While the Columbia Broadcasting System was considering an option, an abrupt change in network policy and personnel ended that project. The National Council of Churches toyed with the idea of maintaining a professional choral organization but that, too, failed to materialize. My finances were fast dwindling as I began to perceive an indefinable change in the atmosphere of offices and conference rooms and in the attitude of executives who received me. The time was not right for the projects I proposed, regardless of how attractive they might be. I indulged myself in a moment of pure panic before settling down to consider the state of poverty I was about to enjoy.

My work with Althouse gave me a focal point, and I convinced myself that all was not disaster. Of course, I had no job, very little money, and a lease on an apartment I could not afford, but surely, if I dug about, something would turn up. I began to dig. I called Dr. Williamson, who was still president of Westminster Choir College and who had followed my work in the South with interest and encouragement. He knew of no opening for a choir director in the metropolitan area, but he promised to keep me advised of any possibilities. I could teach voice production and breathing technique, but building a roster of pupils would take months and years which I currently did not have to spare. I adopted the time-honored custom of reading the "Help Wanted" ads. My youth had not been afflicted with affluency and there were many things I could do.

I was negotiating a job as display manager in a men's clothing shop when Dr. Williamson telephoned late one evening to tell me of a potential opening for a choir director in Bay Ridge, Brooklyn. The Evangelical Lutheran Church of the Good Shepherd wanted to reactivate its former Westminster program of integrated choirs and was in search of a director willing to undertake the reorganization of choirs of all age levels. I wasted not a moment in making an appointment with the minister of the church. My background so impressed him that he assured me of the job as soon as a few necessary details were attended.

Time required for the necessary details wore on and on. When I was near desperation, the call came to ask if I could have ready for the traditional Christmas Candlelight Service an integrated choir program involving six choirs, ages three-and-a-half years on up. I looked at the calendar. The service was slightly more than four weeks away.

Necessity being what necessity is, I figured that not trying was worse than failure. After I had agreed to attempt the task, I found that active membership in the six choirs totaled a little over two dozen. With the aid of the Choir Guild, which had remained more active than the choirs, I was able to assemble nearly two hundred children, young people, and adults for the service. The Candlelight, as the occasion is termed, was not a major musical triumph, but from the standpoint of logistics and of the vitality it poured back into the congregation, it was a singular success. This was not the job I might have anticipated, but at least I finally was more or less gainfully employed. I agreed to accept certain financial arrangements with the understanding that I be free to determine my own work schedule and to augment my income in any manner I chose.

I chose to offer private instruction in voice production and breathing technique. With the church stipend as a basic income I could take the time necessary to establish a reputation and a following, and I would have a latitude of freedom in which to develop my interest in sound, both choral and individual, and in breathing.

11

GROWTH AND DEVELOPMENT

Although my swift descent upon New York had seemed a near catastrophe, I found during the next several years of growth and development that what I had thought I wanted would have been the catastrophe. The times were changing and I was changing with them. I had to abandon some old ideas for new and clarify my thoughts on a number of points. When my personal ambitions began to conflict with one another, I had to pause for inventory and reorientation.

After the big roundup for the Candlelight Service at the church came an intense moment of cold reckoning. Many years prior to my arrival the church had had an excellent choir program, but over at least a decade the program had deteriorated for one reason or another. Older members of the congregation, remembering the days of glory, resisted the plain facts of the present. My freedom of operation did not fit their concept of wages and hours, and the financial fray began almost before the wax of the Christmas candles had hardened.

In happy contrast, those who had been caught up in the enthusiasm of the sudden revival of the music rallied to my support. From the conglomeration of souls participating in the

Candlelight Service I sorted out six choirs according to ages
and began to organize a program of instruction for each. The
idea behind the Westminster integrated choir program is that
children be taken at an early age (three-and-a-half years in the
Good Shepherd Cherub Choir) and trained musically and
vocally for choral work to the end that the church have a self-
perpetuating adult choir. As the children grow up through the
choirs, their musical knowledge and vocal ability increase.

The church, I soon learned, was seething with controversy.
Indifferent as I was, my task of reviving the defunct music
program became more difficult because of it. I was not as free
as I had been promised. Nor were existing conditions precisely
as they had been described to me earlier. I had frequent occasion to ponder the wisdom of trying to develop anything from
such a snarl. My reassurance came from the choirs themselves, for they began to take on a life apart from the conflict
within the church organization.

Throughout this period and possibly because of it, I thought
more seriously in terms of an independent career for myself. My study with Althouse and my analysis of my own
breathing had enabled me to exceed my previous vocal accomplishments. I was beginning to weary of having to cope with
large numbers of people, and the idea of only myself to manage became, accordingly, more attractive. Before I could take
decisive action, Althouse, who had long been in failing health,
died. I was stunned by his death and for a while was incapable
of personal planning.

By this time I had a number of pupils of my own to consider. As I analyzed their voices and breathing patterns, I began to notice how consistently I did the same thing to myself.
When I sang, a part of my mind was trying to listen, and,
simultaneously, another part was trying to analyze. I would

Growth and Development

have condemned this practice in any one of my pupils, for a performer's whole attention must be focused on *what* he is doing, not *how* he is doing it. Little by little I was forced to conclude that in spite of vocal potential I lacked the temperament of the performer. My analytical tendencies served me well as a teacher, but they were detrimental to the performer. I continued to do an amount of solo work, but I abandoned thoughts of a professional concert career. The best part of my decision was that I could give up my laborious and incompatible study of foreign language, an evil necessary to a serious artist.

In the mid-1950's the musical climate grew cool to the professional choral conductor, and I had to accept the fact that my major reason for coming to New York would have to be shelved indefinitely. Organization of the kind of choral group I had wanted would have been sheer folly. I had neither the finances nor the inclination to indulge myself in an ultimate futility.

The elimination of a professional vocal career and a professional career as a choral conductor left me with my job as director of the Good Shepherd Choir School and my private instruction. Wisdom advised concentration of effort in these areas. The more I worked with voices of all ages, the more I observed and learned about breathing and the more interested I became in the functions of the respiratory system. I found that a particular pattern of breathing enabled children to avoid the throat tension which causes the shrill, piping quality in young voices. I began to observe more closely the interplay of the various muscles of breathing and the subsequent effect on the sound of the voice. As my knowledge broadened, my teaching improved and I began to deal increasingly with breathing problems in relationship to the production of sound.

137

By the second Christmas Candlelight Service regular choir membership had settled at two hundred. The quality of the work had gained sufficient attention both in and outside the immediate Bay Ridge community for the various choirs to receive invitations to participate in the larger Brooklyn community programs and in a C.B.S. national television program. The stimulative effect was great, and as I tightened the discipline, to sing in the choirs became a privilege. I worked with the members of every choir weekly to check their breathing and their voice production. The choral tone of the choirs individually and in unison gave me a large measure of satisfaction.

By 1958 the Good Shepherd Choir School had a firmly established reputation for excellence and was recognized in church music circles as an extraordinary achievement for a church in the metropolitan area. My own study and exploration of breathing habits and respiratory function in relationship to the production of sound had led me farther into the field of science and had extended my profession from that of a teacher of voice production to the role of consultant in breathing problems among individuals having no respiratory disease or disorder. I never dealt with respiratory problems involving physical disorder because I knew enough to know how much I did not know. I had witnessed too much damage caused the well by faulty breathing habits to run the risk of dealing in an area with which I was unfamiliar. I suspected that many of the maneuvers devised to make the well aware of a pattern of breathing might be too strenuous for the ill.

When I was asked at this time to undertake the project at East Orange, I hesitated because I did not feel adequate for the task. I disliked hospitals intensely and I knew very well that I was ignorant of the specific effects of disease and disorder upon the respiratory mechanism. I was not certain I wanted to become involved with the ill. The well were difficult enough. While hesitation occupied the fore of my thoughts, curiosity sat spiderlike in a dark corner waiting for the moment to ensnare.

Even as I hesitated, I began to wonder how the breathing of the ill differed from that of the well, whether there were points of basic similarity, if certain effects could be anticipated among the ill as among the well. Inch by inch, hesitation drifted toward the web and in an unguarded moment was devoured by curiosity. When I had overcome the major problem of adapting my schedule to additional activity, I spent a number of weeks in the medical library familiarizing myself with respiratory diseases and disorders and exploring further the literature on breathing and the mechanics of breathing. To my surprise, I found that very little attention had been accorded the act of breathing and its influence on the body since the latter part of the nineteenth century.

From the beginning I had been assured that medical consultation would always be available to me and that I would be under the constant supervision of medical doctors. My great concern was that I not unwittingly inflict damage upon an already damaged respiratory mechanism. If err I must, I wanted it to be on the side of overcaution. When I felt sufficiently prepared academically, I made the first of my numerous journeys to East Orange and began the work which led to the discovery of breathing coordination and the evolution of SIMBIC.

In 1958 I began to live a sort of double life with a triple career that was sometimes confusing to me and, as a rule, totally baffling to those who knew me in a single capacity. During all the years of medical study and research in breathing, I was still serving as director of the Good Shepherd Choir School and teaching voice production and breathing to private pupils. As disparate as those occupations might seem, they were not so at all. My method of teaching voice production, whether for choral or individual work, derived from the use of the muscles of breathing in a particular pattern. Breathing and its effect upon the production of sound were my principal interests. In the adaptation of my teaching methods for the well to the requirements of the ill, I was always listening to the sound of the voice. I am convinced that nothing other than the sound of the voice could have elicited the physical responses and subsequent observations responsible for the discovery of breathing coordination.

I learned to move with ease and freedom back and forth between the world of the well and the world of the ill. My observations in one served to heighten my awareness in the other. I found that I could adapt practices from one to the other. What was effective with emphysema patients had an application in correcting breathing faults of the well. I began to note among my choir members and private pupils irregularities I could identify in the patient as a sure sign of a particular fault or weakness.

The Choir School became a sort of laboratory in which I had the extraordinary opportunity to observe and analyze the breathing habits of every age level. I could put my medical findings into immediate practice and correlate the responses. I did the same thing with my private pupils. To my extreme satisfaction, I saw the breathing improve, with subsequent physical benefits, and I heard the improvement in the sound of the voices. Sometimes my mind raced so that I could hardly keep my jumble of thoughts sorted. Always I was impressed by how little was known of the potentials of breathing and how desperately people needed to know about the influence of breathing upon health and well-being.

Although the Choir School continued to grow and thrive in the early 1960's, the church itself was racked within by dissension and threatened without by the shift in the community which the construction of the Verrazano Narrows Bridge brought about. Beset with problems both at the church and in the medical work in breathing, I often considered very seriously resigning my post at the Choir School and devoting my time solely to private teaching and research. Each time I came to the moment of decision, I realized that working with the great music of the church had a profound influence on my life and thought. I did not know where to turn for an adequate substitute, and I would be the poorer for the loss. I had been associated with church music for so long that I could not imagine passing the Sundays without it. At this point I always decided to endure a little longer in the hope that eventually I might extricate myself from the church's internal affairs and operate the Choir School independently of them.

In 1964, the same year the discovery of breathing coordination was announced, the Good Shepherd combined choirs accepted an invitation to provide the choral music for the dedication of the Protestant-Orthodox Center at the New York World's Fair. Everyone thought that was the year of matchless glory. So did I.

We all were wrong. Heights still remained to be scaled. In 1965, the year The Stough Institute was founded, the Good Shepherd combined choirs were invited to participate in the brotherhood program sponsored by the National Conference of Christians and Jews in the Singer Bowl of the World's Fair. The occasion was unique in that it was the first ecumenical choral concert to be presented after the Roman Catholic restrictions were relaxed. Both racial and religious integration contributed further to the singularity of the concert, which I was asked to coordinate. That year the Good Shepherd combined choirs were also included in the recording "Great Choirs of New York," made as a special commemorative album for the Protestant-Orthodox Center at the Fair.

As I had hoped, each successive choral achievement drew the Choir School more and more apart from those church affairs with which it had no direct concern. Through the years I had developed a training program and a loyal group of volunteer aids that made possible the efficient operation of the school on a concentrated schedule; otherwise, I should never have been able to continue the choral work, regardless of my desire.

After the Institute began operations and entered into investigations of the breathing habits of the physically superior, the weeks never seemed to be long enough for all that had to be crowded into them. The Choir School received invitations to participate in a variety of activities, and whenever possible I accepted because of the stimulus the young and the old alike derived from public appearances. However, the regular church schedule was so demanding that very little time remained for outside activities.

When the Institute went into the athletic studies in cooperation with the Olympic Committee, I again thought of resigning the Choir School, but the enthusiastic support the choirs received plus my old personal considerations made me decide to continue as long as was feasible. I reasoned that there would be no outside activities and that with careful planning I should be able to maintain the high standards I demanded for the regular program. If I had to lower the standards, that would be the unmistakable indication that the time had come for me to stop.

Basically, there was nothing wrong with that reasoning insofar as I could see. My only error was that I had failed to reckon on the unexpected. I did not expect the unexpected, and, naturally, the unexpected came to pass. The Manhattan Division of the Protestant Council of Churches asked me to accept the responsibility of the choral music for the 1967 Easter dawn service at Radio City Music Hall. I quite honestly did not have the time to do the job. On the other hand, knowing what it would mean to the Good Shepherd choirs to sing at Radio City Music Hall, I could not in conscience refuse.

For the Good Shepherd choirs to appear at the Music Hall was not just an exercise in self-gratification. It was rather a curious culmination of circumstance in the life of the church. When the church had enjoyed its original successful choir program some thirty years earlier, the highlight was participation in a choral program in Radio City Music Hall. The wheel had come full circle, and who was I to say nay? I did not know how I would manage to get the program organized and presented, but I accepted. Later, I was glad that I had. The experience proved to be a high adventure for everyone.

During those scrambled years of shuttling back and forth from one career to another, the chief hazard was one not of passage but of identification. Because no one could accept the field of breathing as a legitimate field of science in critical need of exploration, no one could understand how I could deal on the one hand with the sound of the human voice and on the other with the respiratory problems of the chronically ill. The bridge over which I passed quite readily from the world of music or sound into the world of medicine or disease was the act of breathing. In the world of music I used breathing as a control for sound. In the world of medicine I used breathing and sound to relieve the distress characteristic of respiratory disease. But what was I? Who was I?

I certainly was not the usual musician absorbed in musical scores. Nor was I a doctor absorbed in medicine. No one from either field could do what I did, and no one from either field was aware that I was working assiduously in a third field, the field of breathing, which had significant application in both the others. Until the medical research that resulted in the discovery of breathing coordination and the development of SIMBIC, the field of breathing was an uncharted territory of assorted theories and practices and very little scientific investigation or exploration. My identification as a respiratory consultant baffled the people who knew me only in my capacity as Choir School director although they might be well aware of my work in medicine. People in the medical field who did not know how I had got there in the first place were equally baffled. All in all, I was for a long time a source of perplexity for friends, acquaintances, and colleagues equally.

As the importance of breathing patterns and habits in a civilization of ever-mounting respiratory hazards has become more generally recognized and stressed, my role of respiratory consultant has taken on a new significance. Dyspnea—breathlessness—cannot be medicated, nor can consistent sound be produced without proper management of the breathing mechanism. Between those two boundaries lie all the intricate ramifications and countless applications of breathing coordination.

144

12

THE TRAILER IN THE
LONESOME PINES

Late spring of 1968 was a frenzied time for everyone connected with Olympic planning. The days were flying by and each that passed unfulfilled was a treasure lost. As the Olympic coaches deliberated the inclusion of SIMBIC in the high altitude regimen, Giegengack's impatience surpassed my own. He was going to participate in the South Lake Tahoe program and was as eager as I to know what it would include. One by one the coaches accorded SIMBIC their enthusiastic approval until finally only one remained for the required unanimity. When I was completely numbed by the suspense, the crucial consent was given.

The ideal procedure would have been for me to have instructed the coaches in SIMBIC and for them, in turn, to have instructed the athletes. However, that was not possible because of the intricacies of establishing breathing coordination. I had not had the time necessary to develop a teacher-training program, and I knew from my work with doctors that learning how to breathe in a properly coordinated pattern did not qualify an individual to teach. Clear as that fact was to anyone familiar with SIMBIC, it was difficult for others to accept, particularly so when it limited the numbers to be taught.

145

Gieg, continuing in his accustomed role of SIMBIC interpreter, dispatched this bulletin: "I have undertaken some ten sessions of this remarkable procedure with Mr. Stough, and our very knowledgeable trainer, Bill Dayton, has had some fourteen sessions. Despite this instruction and despite our own very sizable improvement in vitality, neither Bill nor I feel that we are well enough educated in this procedure to make us teachers of it. Consequently, it appears to be of no value to have Mr. Stough instruct some of our coaches, and I am convinced that he himself must directly instruct the individual athletes if we are to realize the real benefits."

The final hurdle cleared, planning could get down to the details. Since my principal work in athletics had been in track and field and Gieg was vice chairman of the Men's Olympic Track and Field Committee, quite naturally I was assigned to this event. Instruction would begin with athletes who required more than two minutes of maximum effort and quicker recovery and would be extended as the schedule permitted to other areas according to exertion and/or recovery needs. Some eighty athletes would require from five to eight sessions of thirty to forty-five minutes each over a period of six weeks. I would be instructing from eight to twelve athletes daily, seven days a week. I was so pleased to come at last to my long-desired exploration of the respiratory condition and habits of human beings of superior physical endowment, world champions and potential world champions, that I did not pause to consider the prodigious amount of work before me. Whatever had to be done, I would find a way to do.

Upon that happy note of resolution I charted my course for South Lake Tahoe in the High Sierra of California. My previous travels in the Far West had been limited to the coastal area; therefore, I was unprepared for my experience in the highlands. At that time, entry to South Lake Tahoe was through Reno, Nevada, aboard an airport service conveyance which operated irregularly on a regular schedule. The vehicle broiled in the July sun for an hour past its scheduled departure while waiting for an overdue plane from Denver. The internal temperature must have been in the range of 120 degrees Fahrenheit when the passengers took their seats and the driver, starting the motor, issued strict instructions to keep the windows up for speedy air conditioning. The wonders of the Nevada terrain were wasted on me that trip in the wheeled oven, but by the time we were curving around the mountains in approach to Lake Tahoe, the speedy air conditioning had begun to work and my sensory receptors were reactivated. The lake lying among the majestic mountains beneath a cloudless blue sky intensified the blue in its waters. Towering pines stood like august sentinels across the mountain slopes and along the shores. The incredible beauty was then and later a source of deep refreshment.

I never recovered from the utter grandeur of the mountains and the sparkle of sunlight in the clear dry air. Conditioned as I was to the dull yellow light of the metropolitan gas chambers, I felt that I was participating in a recurrent miracle each day. The overpowering natural beauty all about made possible a concentration of effort which otherwise would have been difficult to maintain.

Gieg had preceded me and at 8:30 on the morning after my arrival was ready to be off and running. I had anticipated a fast start but his pace exceeded my expectations. Without SIMBIC to cut my own warm-up time, I should have dropped with the starting gun that day. He had scheduled an instant orientation program calculated to put me three days ahead by noon of the first day. I made a mighty effort to absorb all the sights and sounds and to try to remember some of the names. I received a briefing on Tahoe topography, an introduction to local officials involved in the high altitude program, an introduction to Olympic officials, coaches, doctors, and trainers, a quick glimpse of my living quarters, and a tour of the areas of athletic activities.

When I had sat in New York and contemplated the summer project, I had envisaged a sort of neat compound with all facilities within convenient walking distance. The only thing within convenient walking distance was my rented car, which carried me faithfully up and down and around all the mountains separating the Olympic facilities one from the other. Dependent upon the flow of traffic, travel time from my quarters to my office could be forty-five minutes, as the snake crawls. The magnificence of the scenery staved off madness in the winding procession of cars and trucks and buses.

The Olympic track, a replica of the track in Mexico City, was located above the sprawling friendly community of South Lake Tahoe at Echo Summit, an elevation of some seven thousand-plus feet above sea level. My office occupied not quite so exalted a position. It was in a place a few hundred feet lower, known as "The Trailers." Here in long trailer units the bachelor athletes lived and froze in the brisk mountain air. My office was in the very last unit of the very last trailer among the tall, lonesome pines. I shared the site with a family of five frisky chipmunks who lived in a hollow pine opposite my door. In due time the formal designation of "office" wore down to the simpler term "trailer."

When Gieg first took me to the trailer to inspect the provisions made for SIMBIC instruction, athletes were there before me waiting to begin. Their enthusiasm cushioned the blow I was about to receive. While the trailer was adequate for teaching purposes, it had none of the specified office facilities required for the maintenance of Olympic records and accumulation of Institute data. I had hoped to have working space for a secretary who could have relieved me of the paper routine, but the restrictions of dimensions made such an arrangement impossible. I would have to do the job myself in the evenings after I had finished teaching. Not a bright prospect, but it would work.

On the day following the instant orientation, I settled into a schedule of sɪᴍʙɪᴄ instruction and related activities that continued unabated week after grinding week. I taught breathing coordination, gave lectures and demonstrations, attended special meetings and required social functions, met the press, appeared on television, served as resuscitator at track meets, and explained repeatedly the functions of the respiratory muscles. I also learned much that I had not known and would never have suspected.

Although the prior athletic studies had shown unmistakably that the best of athletes have respiratory faults and difficulties, I had continued to cherish the notion that in the topmost echelons the physical superiority surely would have a parallel respiratory superiority with accompanying breathing efficiency. It was not precisely so. World champions and potential world champions proved to be as susceptible to respiratory weaknesses as any business or professional man, possibly more so because of the unrelenting demands made upon the respiratory system. These weaknesses in combination with the decreased supply of oxygen in the air at high altitude posed a very real problem for men whose performance ability depended on the amount of oxygen available to the body for energy. Here at the opposite end of the pole from the emphysema patient the need for breathing efficiency was equally as great.

I searched continually for the perfectly coordinated, fully developed breathing mechanism, and I came very close to it upon occasion. Even in those rare cases of perfectly coordinated breathing, the respiratory apparatus was not developed to full potential, and improper management under the stress of extreme exertion destroyed the coordination and introduced a breathing pattern of damaging inefficiency. Although everyone associated with athletics was aware of the importance of breathing in athletic performance, no one whom I met, including coaches, trainers, and attendant physicians, had more than a passing acquaintance with the sketchiest of fundamentals of the respiratory system and the mechanics of breathing. For most, the lungs were a kind of oxygen-supplying machine, and as long as they supplied oxygen on demand, nothing more could be of great consequence. The prevailing ignorance of the profound relationship between the basic mechanics of breathing and the other body functions troubled me constantly because it fostered a thoughtless abuse of the respiratory system. In some, the threat to health and safety under the stress of extreme exertion at high altitude was immediate. In others, long-range damage to the respiratory mechanism was a definite possibility.

Despite all my former notions, I had to acknowledge that physical superiority does not predicate breathing efficiency, that development of voluntary muscles rarely has a corresponding development of the involuntary muscles. That realization certainly did not contribute to my happiness. On the contrary, it filled me with an uneasy sense of urgency. I taught seven days a week all day long and often into the night, yet there was not time enough to see everyone who should have had SIMBIC instruction. After the Tahoe program got under way, the need for SIMBIC in the recovery period regardless of the duration of exertion became apparent. I found myself assuming responsibility for the respiratory condition of the entire contingent of Olympic candidates, particularly as I grew to know them well.

In physical make-up Olympic candidates do not differ appreciably from any well-trained and well-disciplined athlete. They are not perfect. Far from it. They bear the same scars of the unending respiratory battle from birth to death as does the ordinary citizen. They have their share of coughs and colds, and they are just as liable to structural faults and deficiencies as anyone. Case histories of those in the SIMBIC program revealed a variety of respiratory disturbances: allergies, pneumonias, bronchitis, asthma, recurrent and constant colds. Weakened diaphragms were not uncommon, and tensions were prevalent.

The distinguishing characteristic of the Olympic candidate is a demoniac drive to excel himself and to win. Physical pain is ruled out completely. A runner will run when he should be in bed because of his physical condition. A jumper would jump with a broken leg if he could. Nothing short of complete immobilization keeps these men from performance. The agonies of recovery from extreme exertion are known only to themselves.

The men were good SIMBIC pupils. Because of their excellent muscular coordination they learned breathing coordination very readily and were able to incorporate it into their performance rapidly with sometimes astonishing results. One decathlon man left a SIMBIC instruction session, went up to the track to work out, and broke his previous performance record.

151

Another broke his lifetime record in four events in his practice sessions. A five-thousand-meter man who had been training for only seven months because of injuries was soon running less than sixty seconds off the world record. Most of the men reported increased relaxation during workouts, even at maximum.

After the SIMBIC program was under way, the trailer in the lonesome pines was seldom lonesome. Athletes came with all manner of breathing problems to be remedied, some serious, some not so serious. Before the first week was out, the comprehensive view of the human respiratory condition which I had hoped to achieve was complete. I marveled that mortals so totally dependent upon oxygen for life could be so carelessly free of regard for the process of breathing.

13

SLAYING THE DRAGON

Within a matter of days the tall-timbered slopes of Echo Summit became the "Summit," or more simply, the "track." There the wind kicked up dust devils and shook out dry needles from the pines. There from early morning until the last slanting of sun over the mountains, men ran and jumped and vaulted and hurled with incredible endurance. There also lurked a dragon. Not a terrible fire-breathing, tail-lashing, snorting sort of dragon, but a very small, quiet dragon sat in the shadows and waited. Everyone knew of him. No one spoke of him.

My busy schedule did not often permit me to go up to the track, but I suppose I knew more about the dragon than anyone else. He could engender a paralyzing fear in the best of runners and throw a hurdler off pace. He did not have to do anything. The mere fact of his being shriveled away resolution. He needed to be slain. Although I was not given to going about the country dragon-slaying, I decided that something very definitely had to be done about this fellow.

In extreme physical exertion of the kind that took place at the track was the ever-present danger of incurring an oxygen debt. As the name suggests, an oxygen debt is an amount of oxygen the body owes itself after having spent in performance more than it could supply for that performance. To suffer an oxygen debt at sea level is an excruciating experience. No one knew what the effect of the rarefied atmosphere of high altitude would be. This fear of the unknown was the dragon that caused the stoutest heart to tremble. With the proper weapon the dragon could be slain.

The proper weapon with which to slay the dragon was breathing coordination. Athletes who knew how to manage their breathing during the crucial recovery period following performance could avoid an oxygen debt. Freed of energy-absorbing anxieties, they would have an extra measure of energy to put into performance. The first thing I had to do in instructing Olympic candidates at Tahoe was the first thing I had to do with all pupils: make them aware of the breathing mechanism and its functions so that they would understand what they were doing and be able to maintain coordination under varying conditions. When they knew what to do during recovery and could do it, they could escape the psychological shackles forged by fear of the unknown and pace themselves at their best.

Breathing coordination can be taught to pupils who do not have the foggiest notion of the structure of the respiratory mechanism or of the muscles of breathing. Usually, however, a rudimentary knowledge of what is going on inside the body makes both teaching and learning easier. At one time I had assumed that everyone knew a little something about breathing. Experience compelled me to revise that assumption and provide an introduction to the mechanics of breathing. When a pupil can visualize the operation of a muscle, he can bring about a response with increased speed and ease.

The diaphragm is perhaps the best known and the least

known of the muscles of breathing. Closely associated as it is with respiration, it has fallen victim to simplified textbook illustrations of the respiratory system. Often it appears to be a hump under the rib cage to the front of the body. This view of the diaphragm fosters the idea that it operates like a rubber band, pulling the ribs in and out. Another concept, arising from observation of the mid-regions of the body during breathing, is that the protrusion and recession of those regions are due to the outward-inward motion of the diaphragm. Observation of external body movements may be accurate, but the inference of the internal diaphragmatic motion is not.

Generally conceded to be the principal muscle of breathing, the diaphragm extends through the body and divides the thoracic cavity, which contains the rib cage, the lungs, and the heart, from the abdominal cavity, which contains the other vital organs. In addition to its role in breathing, it also has the important function of regulating the pressure between the thoracic and abdominal areas. It can be made to act by the force of voluntary muscles, such as the abdominal, upon it, but it cannot be controlled by the will. For this reason, breathing exercises which increase diaphragmatic motion by use of other muscles can have only a temporary effect on the diaphragm and can cause further damage in the case of a weakened diaphragm.

Motion of the diaphragm is downward toward the abdominal cavity on the inhale and upward into the thoracic cavity on the exhale. In the exhale position, which is the relaxed position of the muscle, the diaphragm is like a dome rising into the rib cage to aid in the expulsion of air from the lungs. On the inhale the dome tends to flatten. If the diaphragm has become weakened through injury of any sort, it does not rise dome-like into the thoracic cavity on the exhale but lies flattened like a piece of rubber that has lost its elasticity. Often a weakened diaphragm will buckle on an exhale and move downward, causing a protrusion of the lower abdomen.

Other muscles of breathing fall into two groups: those used primarily for inhale and those used primarily for exhale. All of the muscles of breathing were intended to operate in a synergistic pattern with the stress of the work load distributed evenly among them. This is breathing coordination, which provides the maximum efficiency of the particular mechanism with the minimum expenditure of energy. When the muscles are not so coordinated, they function in varying patterns with varying degrees of efficiency. The variances may be due to any number of causes, and they can have any number of effects. Chief among the effects is the reliance upon accessory muscles of breathing, with the use of voluntary muscles to force respiratory action and with risk of subsequent damaging alterations of the respiratory mechanism which will increase susceptibility to respiratory infections and pave the way for respiratory disorder and disease.

In operation, one group of involuntary muscles acts with the descending and flattening diaphragm to bring about the expansion and inflation of the lungs with air. The other group produces the exhale or expulsion of air from the lungs and is aided by the return of the diaphragm to its upward or dome-like position. Weakness in any of the muscles will affect the breathing and decrease the efficiency of the respiratory function. Contrary to popular belief, the more important phase of breathing is the exhale. Stale air containing the waste products of the body must be removed from the lungs before new air containing oxygen can be taken in. When the removal of the old air is inefficient, the supply of new air is proportionately reduced. When the removal of the old air is insufficient to meet the body's demands for new air, a smothering sensation results and triggers a frantic drive to take in more air before the lungs are properly emptied. This is the state of dyspnea, or breathlessness, experienced by emphysema patients and Olympic champions alike.

In the trailer at Lake Tahoe the Olympic candidates learned as rapidly as I could teach them to prolong the exhale and empty the lungs as nearly as possible before trying to re-fill them. Some developed their breathing coordination to such a degree and so incorporated it into their performance that they were in effect recovering during performance and did not come to a state of extreme depletion at the end. Others who had not achieved such a state of development or who had temporarily lost their coordination because of some con-dition of performance knew what to do with their breathing in the recovery period to restore coordination and ease the recovery.

One of the best aids I had in teaching was a set of clinical photographs of an advanced emphysema patient who had been the subject of a specialized study completed at the West Haven hospital a few months earlier. The photographs showed the patient prior to breathing coordination instruction, a drawn, wasted figure with chest and shoulders raised, neck and upper chest muscles taut in effort to breathe, and ab-domen grotesquely distended. In the comparison views taken nine months later at the conclusion of the SIMBIC study, the man was almost unidentifiable as the same person. The muscular distortions had disappeared, the chest and shoulders were lowered, the abdomen had flattened, and the skeletal appearance had been transformed.

When an athlete began SIMBIC instruction, I had him take

a look at the photographs and remarked, "Those 'before' photographs are you at the end of competition, grabbing for breath, trying to recover. There is no difference between you in recovery and an advanced emphysema patient trying to breathe."

The effect was powerful. Any lingering doubts about the necessity of intelligent management of breathing were dispelled. My emphysema patient, who could never have survived the rigors of Echo Summit, became a driving force for the intrepid young men who aspired to the gold medals of Mexico City. He made my point for me more dramatically than a thousand words of explanation.

Within a dozen days or so after activities began at South Lake Tahoe, the first track meet was scheduled in order to give the men an opportunity to compete under high altitude conditions and to enable the staff to observe the effects of competition. I could hear the little dragon stirring in the pines, moving in closer to the track to watch and wait. He was not without his victims. One eastern collegiate champion who was not then in the SIMBIC program had not been able to equal his sea level time in practice because he was reluctant to push himself at altitude. Others came to me with their fears about the consequences of extreme exertion, and my schedule was filled up to starting time with extra SIMBIC sessions.

During a pre-meet session a walker whose enthusiasm for SIMBIC almost matched his enthusiasm for his sport instructed me to "be right out there along side of the track, and if you see me do anything wrong, you just come on over and walk next to me and get me straightened out."

He was a walker of international reputation and could set a mean pace. My mental view of the pair of us swinging around the track elbow to elbow while the officials gasped and the spectators guffawed nearly destroyed my composure, but I assured him that I would be on hand in case of emergency.

I fully intended to be on hand because I knew the weaknesses of the men I worked with, and I anticipated that some of them would have difficulty maintaining their coordination during recovery. I also wanted to discourage the use of oxygen as a recovery aid. Far from being an aid, it increases the gas content of lungs already overdistended with unexpelled air and provides a very real threat of suffocation.

Directly from my final session with an edgy runner I went up to the track on my mission of mercy and started out across the finish line in the direction of the green medical tent in the infield. I had not taken a dozen steps before an imposing police officer confronted me, took one look at my drab civilian garb, and advised me to clear the track. That was my first taste of the efficiency of the local security. Although it compelled my admiration, it also exhausted my ingenuity, for I failed altogether to convince the man of the legitimacy of my presence. I verged on withdrawal when a friendly official spotted me and swooped down to the rescue, hustling me over to the medical tent with the advice that I had better get myself an official suit. I never did get an official suit, but Gieg, then serving as coordinator of the USOC Medical Testing and Study Center, lent me the jacket he had worn as head coach of the 1964 Tokyo Olympics. That turned the trick and spared me further encounters with conscientious guardians of the local regulations. I had attained identity.

The results of the first track meet of the high altitude program were very encouraging. Six of the men in the SIMBIC project reported faster recovery than they had experienced before at sea level and marveled at their newly-acquired ability to control their breathing under stress. Three were winners in their events. The effects of SIMBIC were becoming increasingly apparent, particularly under the stringent demands of competition.

After the first track meet the atmosphere cleared. The wind seemed freer and the deep pine shadows less ominous. SIMBIC had overcome the fear of high altitude effects of oxygen debt and had slain the dragon.

14

A LOOK
AT THE ATHLETE

When the dust of the first Tahoe track meet had settled, I took a long appraising look at the athlete and his problems of breathing. The day was fast approaching for a SIMBIC progress report to the Institute and the Olympic Committee, and I needed to sort my thoughts and observations in preparation for the task. I had been so absorbed in starting the SIMBIC instruction that I had had very little opportunity for reflection.

Training at high altitude, I realized, held a curious advantage for many athletes. The men themselves were not aware of it, because they were not looking for that kind of advantage. Most thought of breathing primarily in terms of how much air they could inhale to fill their need. Altitude, then, would be considered a foe rather than a friend because it limited the supply of available oxygen. The unrecognized beneficial effect was that altitude served as a giant magnifying glass to exaggerate all the breathing problems which would have remained obscure at sea level.

Eighty-six per cent of the men with whom I worked were ignorant of the existence of a problem, yet over half of them had abnormally raised chests and most were breathing entirely with accessory muscles during maximum exertion. Twenty per cent had pronounced sternal angles. These abnormalities duplicate those of the respiratory patient. At sea level conditions the athlete might have continued for an indefinite period without consciousness of any irregularity, but a problem would have arisen eventually when the respiratory system became severely overtaxed. At altitude with breathing more difficult, the problems showed immediately and could be corrected.

Apart from all the specific concerns related to athletes and their breathing, I was most troubled by the lack of accurate knowledge of breathing. Misconceptions abounded, as did practices more harmful than beneficial. The most prevalent false assumption was that what comes easily must be all right. If breathing presented no immediate problem, it was put in the "all right" category and dismissed. Thus was much energy wasted, much unnecessary damage risked and often incurred.

The existing respiratory condition of the athlete was never taken into consideration as the prime requisite for adaptation to high altitude. Various theories posited concerning the ease and rate of adjustment encompassed everything but breathing, yet adjustment ease and rate are in direct ratio to the functional efficiency of the breathing mechanism. One athlete could adapt to altitude in a day or so with no difficulty. Another of the same general physical condition and performance ability needed more time. The difference, which went completely unrecognized, was in the state of the respiratory mechanism and the effectiveness of its operation. The capability of some athletes to adjust readily often requires others who cannot adapt with equal ease to perform too soon. Failure to consider respiratory condition is always a potentially dangerous omission.

Inevitably breathing faults or irregularities are accentuated in performance because the voluntary muscles which under other conditions would lend support to the involuntaries are actively engaged in performance and the burden of breathing falls to the involuntaries. Any weakness in the involuntaries will be increased by the constantly repeated demands of extreme exertion. Even the well-coordinated "natural" athlete who may have unusually well-coordinated breathing can lose his breathing pattern under the stress of exertion. Unless he can manage his breathing intelligently, he will go into accessory breathing to supply the increased need of his body for oxygen.

SIMBIC begins with correction of breathing faults and develops the involuntary muscles to sustain the breathing during performance. If the coordination is lost in some erratic movement of exertion, the athlete trained in SIMBIC is aware of the loss and knows how to regain his coordination without falling into accessory breathing and jeopardizing his recovery.

At Tahoe breathing faults and irregularities were the rule among the athletes. I found very few who needed only to develop their breathing coordination, and even they were managing their breathing by chance rather than by accurate knowledge of what they were doing. One of the most common faults was the use of the voluntary muscles to force the operation of the involuntaries. So-called "diaphragmatic" and belly breathing rely on the use of the abdominal muscle to pump air out and in the lungs. This maneuver serves to exert an excess of pressure on the diaphragm and to promote further weakness where weakness already exists. Moreover, in performance the abdominal muscle is involved in other activity and cannot be employed fully in breathing. If the muscles of breathing are not properly developed, they cannot support the additional work load.

Another tendency was to carry the shoulders high, a posture which distorted the muscular pattern and restricted the expansion of the rib cage. Accessory breathing was inevitable under such conditions. Athletes susceptible to this fault cut their oxygen intake and made themselves candidates for oxygen debt. Many men held their breath at some point in performance. Breath-holding is a state of suspension in which the gaseous wastes of the body's activities accumulate as the oxygen supply is cut off. Indicative of a lack of body control, it contributes to build-up of tensions and creates within the lungs air pressure damaging to the alveoli, or air cells. For efficient function of both body and mind, breathing should be constantly maintained in a rhythmical pattern according to physiological requirements.

Opposite breath-holding is hyper-ventilation, a malpractice frequently employed in a misguided attempt to increase the body's supply of oxygen for performance. Ironically, the net result of the attempt is a build-up of carbon dioxide, the very waste product of which the athlete needs to rid himself. Hyper-ventilation fills the lungs with unusable air, taxes the respiratory mechanism with the expulsion of the excess air, and abuses the breathing muscles by forced breathing. The practice achieves nothing resembling the effects of a coordinated pattern.

Swimmers, in particular, are given to the combined evils of hyper-ventilation and breathing suspension, thereby necessitating both an exhale and an inhale on the turn. After the Yale swimmers had developed their breathing coordination, they used a prolonged exhale before the inhale for the dive and exhaled as they swam. On the turn they were ready for an immediate inhale. Effectiveness of the change in practice was evident in improved performances.

Whatever the breathing fault, once the Olympic candidate had it pointed out to him, he could make the correction rapidly. As the men in the SIMBIC program developed their breathing coordination, they began to recover faster and could take more strenuous workouts more frequently than they could at sea level. When they had integrated SIMBIC into their performance, they could pinpoint their breathing problems and solve them satisfactorily.

Within two instruction sessions Rick Sloan, a decathlon man, was able to correct himself as he began to grab for breath and lapsed into accessory breathing during a workout in the hills. Reestablishing coordination, he ran up the hill for the first time and thereafter could take the ascent in stride. He had easy recoveries and in a day or two broke his life records for three events. He adapted his breathing very quickly to the demands of the various events and could manage far more strenuous workouts than he had been able to previously.

A four-hundred-meter hurdler came to a SIMBIC session with the problem of inability to maintain his breathing coordination from warm-up through the start of the race. After he was over the third hurdle, he could regain his coordination and keep it throughout the competition, but until that point he floundered and cut his speed. On analyzing his problem, he found that he was holding his breath in the blocks waiting for the starting gun. I suggested that he try a long, relaxed exhale while waiting, then at the gun the inhale would be automatic and his rhythmical pattern would be established. We also discussed several other possibilities, and from these he was able to handle his problem successfully.

Not only did the first track meet emphasize various faults

in breathing, it underscored the dangers of oxygen debt and the necessity of intelligent recovery management to avoid the serious possible consequences of such a debt. An even greater need was intelligent handling of athletes who did not know how to manage their breathing and who had difficulty in recovering from an oxygen debt. I had witnessed their agonies and had been appalled by the unintelligent management.

During recovery from extreme physical exertion an athlete who cannot breathe efficiently enough to meet his body's increased need for oxygen to avoid toxic build-up will go into a painful and dangerous state of oxygen debt. The condition can continue for a longer or shorter period of time, according to its management. In the initial stages the athlete suffers such severe leg pains that he cannot stand without support. He must be kept in motion, for loss of consciousness with resulting immobility makes possible a toxic accumulation capable of causing kidney damage or heart attack. In this stage he should be encouraged to extend the exhale as long as he can and keep his back muscles operative to permit expansion of the rib cage.

In the intermediary stages the athlete experiences extreme nausea. At this point he may lie down, but he must keep the back motion of breathing, for this motion can be felt and can serve as his guide in maintaining a rhythmical pattern. Severe headache characterizes the final stages of oxygen debt and may be accompanied by blurred vision or difficulty in focusing. One athlete described his vision reaction as, "it looks like the ground is coming up at you in angles." Here a pattern of steady rhythmical breathing is essential to restoration of oxygen balance and speed of recovery.

Administration of oxygen as an antidote for oxygen debt is a dangerously unwise measure. Many athletes will refuse it instinctively. It tends to nauseate, and it holds the ever-present threat of suffocation by additional filling of lungs already congested with unexpelled gases. Dyspnea, or breathlessness, in athlete or respiratory patient requires for relief an emptying of the lungs through prolonged exhalation, not further filling.

Another revelation of the first track meet was that sprinters were particularly susceptible to oxygen debt. In their short period of violent exertion the body had no chance to feed back into itself any part of the oxygen expended in the effort of competition. When the race was run, they were left gasping in the thin air, and most had no idea what to do other than gasp until the body's demands for oxygen were met. The SIMBIC program had been premised upon the endurance needs of athletes exerting energy over a span of time. No one had foreseen that the longer span of endurance would act in the athlete's favor by enabling him to apply SIMBIC and, in effect, make a constant recovery during performance. My schedule would have to be expanded to include more men.

Watching the effects of SIMBIC over the early days of the program, I became more acutely aware of the far-reaching influences of breathing on the other actions and reactions of the body. With the establishment of breathing coordination and the subsequent development of the muscles of breathing, many of the complaints of the athletes disappeared. I could conclude from my knowledge of the respiratory development and from the disappearance of the complaint what had caused the complaint originally.

I found a surprisingly common respiratory deficiency among athletes to be diaphragmatic weakness. It shows up under exertion as side stitches, abdominal pain, and nausea. It can be detected by protrusion of the abdomen on the exhale. When the diaphragm is weakened, it is unable to support the pressures of breathing and to maintain stabilized pressure in the abdominal cavity. As pressures build in the abdominal area and center upon various points, the familiar side stitches, abdominal pain, and nausea of exertion result. With the development of the diaphragm through SIMBIC they disappear.

Two of the top five-thousand-meter men suffered side stitches and abdominal pain. One was compelled to drop out of two races because of severe upper abdominal pain with side stitches in the lower left quadrant. After three SIMBIC sessions each of the men reported that he no longer experienced pain while running.

The many and various side effects of SIMBIC seemed like a kind of witchery to the Olympic candidates, who had expected only to be taught a new pattern of breathing to speed their warm-up and recovery and perhaps aid their performance. Word spread around that a good thing was going up there in the last trailer at the Summit. I never knew when a strange face would appear around the door frame and request "some of those breathing lessons." Often one enthusiastic athlete would bring a friend for instruction. The openings in my schedule were filled before they occurred.

I had only to consider my own initial errors in thinking of athletes to understand the errors of sports personnel. Superior physical development and coordination would seem to indicate that the breathing must be in good order although the opposite is too frequently true. Muscular overdevelopment, particularly in the chest area, can restrict breathing by hindering the motion of the rib cage. The involuntary muscles of breathing cannot be developed by any applied external force, muscular or otherwise, and it sometimes happens that a superior physique houses a weakened, inefficient breathing mechanism.

Breathing efficiency is not a normal condition to be expected of the athlete. Next to the respiratory patient, the athlete who is endlessly making exorbitant demands upon his respiratory mechanism, often under the most adverse of circumstances, is in greatest need of accurate knowledge of breathing and proper breathing practices. Too many former athletes have developed into respiratory patients in later life to ignore the warning signs.

Proper breathing management is not only an essential health and safety measure for the athlete, it is his prime source of energy for performance. His respiratory check-out is as important as his general physical examination.

15

THE SOUNDS OF TAHOE

After the rumble and the roar of New York the sounds of Tahoe were exotic. The ordinary sounds of traffic and daily activities were muted by the vast surrounding space, and in among them were the unexpected: the lowing of cattle in a nearby pasture, the snorting of pack horses along a mountain trail, dry rustling of a giant pine cone shaken free by the wind, soft lapping of Tahoe's icy blue waters against the shore. I grew accustomed to these.

I also grew accustomed to the silences of the Summit interrupted only by occasional voices and the restless wind among the pines. New sounds startled. None was ever so startling as the precise measure of a Bach fugue which floated down from the track area on the warm, dusty air one afternoon. I had gone up from my trailer to watch a runner work out and was rounding the curve to the security checkpoint when the austere music so totally foreign to the folk style of the region infiltrated the quiet stirrings of the forest.

Unbelieving, I paused, then curiosity hurried me on. Seated upon a rock was a small, wiry, bearded young man playing a cello with considerable skill. A SIMBIC pupil, he greeted me gravely and explained that music was a pleasant pastime for an otherwise dull job of security guard. I agreed, commenting that Bach was a welcome relief to the native beat. Whereupon he promptly offered me a choice of tape recordings plus recorder which he had brought with him from the East to meet just such an emergency. I accepted gratefully.

Of all the sounds of Tahoe, undoubtedly the most provocative were those which issued from my busy trailer at the end of the line. Here, daily, might be heard a rich assortment of voices chanting mystically like some Aeolian priests invoking the winds. Actually, they *were* invoking the winds after a fashion and with success. In SIMBIC the ability to produce sound is the gauge of the condition of the muscles used for breathing.

Breathing is the physical function without which nothing is. To make certain that the breathing is continued, the body has been provided with various devices, some completely beyond the control of the will, others within the power of the mind to operate. Most useful of the devices is the production of sound. Breathing can exist without sound, but there can be no voice sound without breathing. The human voice is the flow of air over the contracted vocal cords. In the production of sound the respiratory muscles are compelled to move air from the lungs, simultaneously releasing tension and preparing for the inhale.

The first cry of the newborn infant begins the lifelong operation of the respiratory mechanism. All during life the sharp outburst, as before the shot put, the karate blow, or the combat charge, serves to relieve the resistant, energy-absorbing internal pressures which impede action and to sustain the exhale-inhale cycle. When the breathing mechanism functions with a balance of exhale-inhale, the body can operate more efficiently than with erratic breathing patterns.

All forms of voice sounds—speaking, shouting, mumbling,

humming, singing—tend to promote the breathing. The humming or singing of people at work maintains the exhale-inhale cycle and improves the work performance by providing oxygen for energy and reducing tension. A lonely person talks to himself as much in a compulsive attempt to release the air pressure within the lungs as for companionship. Like any muscles of the body, the muscles of breathing must have appropriate exertion to retain their tone. The baby, who cannot speak, cries not only to voice his protest against the indignities of the world but to develop his respiratory mechanism as well.

Ironically, good may bear evil. Many things which are of benefit properly used can become harmful through improper use. Sound in relationship to the respiratory mechanism is no exception. For those in a state of respiratory health, the production of sound can serve as a stimulus to the breathing mechanism. For those with a respiratory problem, sound production can impose intolerable strain. For anyone, whatever his condition, violent or excessive use of the voice is potentially damaging to the breathing.

When a voice sound is employed in SIMBIC, the vocal cords are the isometric resistance against which the muscles of breathing must act. The resistance of the vocal cords to the column of air expelled from the lungs confines the activity of the muscles to the limits of their strength. As soon as the respiratory muscles are no longer capable of supporting the pressure of the air necessary to make sound, the sound weakens. Efforts to force the sound will damage muscular tone over a time just as will enforced operation of any muscle of the body.

Because of the direct relationship between the ability to produce sound and the condition of the respiratory muscles, the trained ear can determine the general state of the muscles by the quality and intensity of the voice. Body fatigue and stress also affect the operation of the respiratory mechanism and are reflected in the voice. A failure of the voice is a sure indication that something has gone wrong somewhere in the breathing. The most common cause of extended vocal failure is the weakened diaphragmatic muscle. Temporary failure of the voice may be due to any one of a number of physiological or psychological causes which in turn exercise a debilitating effect on the breathing. There are, of course, various throat conditions unrelated to breathing which influence the sound of the voice and can be identified as such.

Having dealt professionally with voice sounds all my adult life, I was acutely aware of the sound of the voices of the emphysema patients at East Orange and of the inability of the patients to sustain sound. From that awareness arose the line of exploration and investigation which resulted in the discovery of breathing coordination. An emphysema patient might have breathed easily, but the moment he began to speak, the abdomen protruded, indicating that the diaphragm could not support the pressure of the air against the resistance of the vocal cords. Instead of rising into the thoracic cavity on the exhale, the diaphragm moved downward beneath the air column, thereby creating pressure in the abdominal cavity. Use of the abdominal muscle in an attempt to force the voice only weakened the diaphragm further. In some patients the voice had faded almost to a whisper.

If the diaphragmatic muscle were to regain tone, it had to be opposed by an isometric force in a mild exercise. The vocal cords were the force, and the system of counting was the "exercise." However, the diaphragm was not being exercised independently in the counting. It operated in a synergistic pattern with the other muscles of breathing. When the respiratory muscles could sustain a certain amount of air pressure, indicated by duration of count on a single breath, the voice began to acquire fundamental pitch and took on an intensity previously lacking. The pronounced change in voice always surprised both the patient and his doctor.

The use of sound to develop the muscles of breathing is fundamental to SIMBIC. As the efficiency of breathing improves, the ability to produce and sustain sound increases and can be a gauge to determine the ability to perform work. The respiratory mechanism can support work performance in direct ratio to voice production. Breathing coordination is self-regulating and within the respiratory limits of the individual will supply the breath required for a particular task. These are the basic principles of SIMBIC.

Breathing coordination cannot be taught with complete success unless sound is used. One of the most difficult assignments I ever had was instruction of a man whose larynx had been removed. I could establish his breathing pattern and correct his breathing faults, but without the voice there was no accurate gauge of the strength of the respiratory muscles nor was there the isometric resistance needed to develop the muscles. Between us we worked out a system of slow exhale, but it was never entirely satisfactory. Other patients failed to realize their full potential because they could not understand the principle of sound production. They complained that the device of counting made them feel foolish and that they were afraid of being overheard. As a result, their muscles of breathing could not be properly developed. At best they could avoid panic in case of breathlessness, for they knew how to manage themselves, but they could tolerate only limited activity.

In contrast to these was the young girl paralyzed below the neck. She not only learned to manage her breathing satisfactorily but developed her respiratory muscles to such a degree that she could sustain the long sounds and different pitches for singing the songs she enjoyed. One Christmas she recorded a selection of her songs as a gift for her friends. Hers was a remarkable achievement by one who prior to SIMBIC had difficulty speaking and had spent much time in a respirator. Singing has become a particular pleasure for her because it is something done without aid from another.

The basis of all my choir work is SIMBIC. Every choir member is checked at every session for proper breathing habits, and over the years the voice development has been rewarding. With proper breathing, the production of sound involves none of the difficulties associated with the training of immature voices. The voice develops in direct measure to the ability of the respiratory muscles to sustain the production of sound. As a small bonus for the choirs, their respiratory habits have helped to improve their health.

Certainly, none of the Olympic candidates in the Tahoe SIMBIC program was prepared for the surprising changes which occurred in their voices with the development of their breathing coordination. Whatever they may have expected of their SIMBIC training, that was not it. Athletes who had weakened diaphragms were especially subject to marked voice changes. Their voices had a thin, breathy quality of sound and tended to be of a higher pitch than would have been anticipated from their well-developed physique. As the muscles of breathing were able to sustain increased air pressure, the voice became fuller and deeper. Release of throat tensions produced by accessory breathing also contributed in a degree to the improvement in the voice. In some instances the change was so noticeable that the athlete's associates commented upon it.

Voice is always the product of the breathing. The so-called "singing" voice is the same as the speaking voice, for singing, basically, is speaking on pitch. When the breathing is coordinated, the singer has his "natural" voice; that is, the sound individually his own. The "natural" voice is distorted as the singer tries to imitate a desired sound rather than develop the sound uniquely his own. Accessory muscles are used to alter the sound and in time the breathing pattern is altered; whereupon, the singer begins to experience the problems of voice production and later may lose his voice.

Modern amplification methods destroy the sound of the natural voice by compelling the singer to make a particular desired sound rather than the sound resulting from his proper breathing and vocal equipment. Many voice teachers whose knowledge of respiratory management is sketchy do the same thing. Countless singers never know the sound of their natural voice because their breathing is faulty and because they attempt to make a sound pleasing to themselves and to their listeners.

A number of the athletes at Tahoe had made voices for themselves by imitating a voice sound which to them seemed to be desirable. As their breathing coordination developed, their voices altered and were more to their liking than the artificial sounds they had been using. The making of a voice may or may not be a conscious effort to reproduce a given sound. In breathing coordination the sound is the result of the action of the air against the vocal cords and is independent of the ear.

Sometimes athletes who followed one another in their simbic sessions did not recognize the changed voices and would peer cautiously through my doorway to see who was inside. At the sight of a friend, the jaw would drop slightly and the eyes widen. An exchange of appropriate comment was sure to follow. Athletics being among the most competitive of

177

life forms, the question was inevitable: "Well, what's *your* count?" Translated roughly, that meant "How good is your breathing?" as indicated by the length of a count achieved on a single breath. And count matching began.

I never did succeed in persuading all the men that the count was not competitive. Because some counted faster than others, it was not how high but how long that mattered. The voicing of numbers was nothing more than a means of producing sound over a measurable period to promote the development of the coordinated respiratory muscles. It was self-limiting because the voice weakened with the exhaustion of the breath. Since each individual differed appreciably, competition was not possible. But the athletes did not see it that way, and tall tales abounded. I did not have the heart to tell them that I was timing them all the while and that an excellent high, attained without any of the boosters they had devised, would have been in the neighborhood of two hundred on a single exhale, timing to some thirty or forty seconds.

The last I heard, a self-declared champion had reached a peak past four hundred. I solemnly congratulated him, for he had made good respiratory progress in attaining that giddy height.

16

DEVILS AND FIENDS

Hidden among the mountains about Lake Tahoe are smaller, tranquil lakes and highland meadows of great beauty. Rustic cabins nestle in the pines along the lake shores and cling to the mountain slopes. Trails wind in and out narrow passes through the great rocks and disappear mysteriously into the forests. The vastness of the mountains engulfs the thousands of campers who come to enjoy the beauty and the peace and to escape their troubles.

Of my first impressions of Tahoe, the most vivid was the prevailing atmosphere of unperturbable calm. The expanse of earth and sky would seem to swallow all the devils and fiends, the pressures and tensions, that tormented "down below," as the uplanders designated the lowlands. I could think of no better place in which to exorcise the demons spawned of the bustle and the hurry of contemporary life. I was not long, however, in discerning the presence of the evil host in our midst. The devils and fiends had come right along with the baggage, and after they had recovered from the jolt of the mountain air, they went about busying themselves with their wicked ways.

The athletes were especially susceptible to the ill effects of tension, both of body and of mind. The physical fatigue which they experienced after a day of workout was not a pleasant exhaustion calculated to give a good night's rest. Too many waste products within the body sensitized the nervous system and made relaxation impossible. Too many pressures and anxieties of top-level competition disturbed the mind for sleep to come readily. A major complaint of the men was sleeplessness which led to further exhaustion and on to more sleeplessness and on and on. Caught up in an endless round of fatigue producing fatigue, they fell ready prey to destructive tensions.

When my SIMBIC pupils clambered the precarious steps to my trailer, their devils and fiends crept over the sill behind them and settled comfortably around the instruction table. Beneath my fingertips I could feel the tense muscles. The voice betrayed the pressures which had accumulated within the body. As the session progressed and the breathing fell into the coordinated pattern, one by one devil and fiend slid quietly off the table and disappeared. Relaxation was nearly always the first impressive sensation of breathing coordination. For many of the athletes, complete relaxation had become a lost art. They had grown so accustomed to their tensions that the feeling of being relaxed was a marvelous new experience for them.

A determined young runner who not only was concerned about his performance in competition but had personal problems as well lay upon my table in an early SIMBIC session and pronounced the ritual of numbers. As his count lengthened, his breathing deepened and his eyes closed. Suddenly he spoke.

"I'm floating!" he announced. "Now I'm floating away! The table's floating, too. We're floating in circles. I never felt like this before in my life!" Eyes still closed, he queried, "Am I here? Am I in the trailer?"

When he returned from his voyage of relaxation, he was

ecstatic over the possibilities which SIMBIC opened to him. He had been ill the year before and had been warned that the outlook on his athletic achievement was not overly bright. He became a very faithful pupil and soon belied the prophets.

Because of the interrelationship of the respiratory system and the nervous system, the condition of one influences the condition of the other. Tension directly affects the breathing mechanism and tends to damage it, causing susceptibility to respiratory complaints and disturbing other systems of the body in turn. As tension mounts, muscles tighten and destructive air pressure builds within the lungs. Unless the pressure is released, nervous mannerisms are manifest and a disturbing interaction of one system upon another is established.

Like the athletes, most people have become so accustomed to their tensions that they are unable to relax. Tension is accepted as a normal condition of contemporary life and is indirectly perhaps the greatest of the destroyers. Speech expressions indicate tension and the need for release. Being "up tight" is a common condition of mankind. Human beings can exasperate one another until "steam comes out of the ears" and they are "red as a beet" or lobster or something equally as vivid. Nerves are "on edge" or "drawn out to thin wires." Given enough pressure, a person is "ready to explode," "blow his top," "flip his lid," "burst a blood vessel," or whatever the current expression is. To avoid such consequences, he is advised to "cool it," "keep calm," "simmer down," "take it easy"—all very good suggestions very hard to follow.

Today the mere fact of being alive is the principal cause of tension. The complexities of modern living breed tension and nurture it. Overcrowding, unending competition for necessities and pleasures, ceaseless attempts to fulfill artificial desires give rise to anger, frustrations, and anxieties which play havoc with the body and mind. Environmental conditions and dietary synthetics add their poisons to the body systems and set in motion the forces of destruction. The deemphasizing of individuality has brought about a loss of regard for self as an independent force in society. Coupled with the grinding drive for success and approval, the loss of self-regard is a guaranteed source of frustration. Life styles and habits have changed faster than the mind can make satisfactory adaptations. With the aggregation of pressures and tensions, the old outlets for them have narrowed correspondingly.

As direct physical action has become more limited, representative action and speech have become more violent. Since men no longer club one another to death, they seek to destroy by social, financial, and psychological means. They vie with each other in minor sports competitions which assume proportions of major military campaigns. They match extravagance with extravagance and race one another down the highways in their big cars. Reason has gone out of fashion and negotiations are conducted in shouts and threats.

The descriptive language of violence is substituted for the act of violence. Those who would not kill freely will declare in a moment of anger, "I'll kill him," or "I'll knock his teeth down his throat," or "I'll beat him to a bloody pulp." The desire to inflict the forbidden punishment or pain is reflected in the speech. In such an atmosphere of suppressed emotions and desires, tensions thrive and must have some form of release.

Most obvious forms are the artificial. Chemicals, alcohols, and drugs induce a certain sense of relief from tension by their action upon the nervous system and upon the mind. Smoking gives a feeling of relaxation with the long exhale of smoke from the lungs. However, the permanent damage often inflicted is hardly worth the temporary relief.

182

As tensions increase, air pressure in the lungs increases. All the forms of producing voice sounds are a natural response to the necessity of releasing the air pressure. The long sigh helps to empty the lungs of waste products and stimulates the breathing, which will give a sense of relief. A nervous person or one ill at ease often tends to laugh too much when laughter is not required, and an excited person will frequently chatter volubly when only a few words are necessary. Crying, with its sometimes rending sobs, leaves the body relaxed by exhausting of air pressures. Easygoing people will whistle or sing or hum. The continual expulsion of air establishes a breathing rhythm which adds to the original sense of well-being. A person in pain may moan or groan to lessen the internal tensions created by the pain. Sound is the safety valve of the body.

Silence is fraught with potential dangers. Maintained over a period of time without a pattern of rhythmical breathing, it builds air pressure into a compulsive force. After the silence of a lecture or a concert or any public assembly the crowd will burst spontaneously into a wild clamor of comment. The silence of a tense moment in a sports competition is always split by an uproar. Children who have maintained a relative quiet during the school day scream and shout in celebration of their freedom. Strangers caught in a tense situation will babble like old acquaintances.

Without the release of the air pressure which the maintenance of long silence builds, unexpelled waste products accumulate in the lungs, the breathing process itself slows, and the oxygen supply to the body is reduced accordingly. All of these factors are damaging to the respiratory system and to other systems of the body as well. Internal air pressure often has an overt effect in the physical sensation of tightening across the upper chest area. When the advice, "Get it off your chest,"

is given, it can be taken quite literally. By helping to expel air
from the lungs, speech relieves the pressure and brings about
a marked physical awareness of relaxed chest muscles. Confession
is good for the soul and even better for the body in that
it terminates the tension-producing silence.

Nowhere is the danger of prolonged silence more apparent
than in dealing with the mentally disturbed. A patient who
does not make voice sounds is restricting his breathing and
creating physical tensions which will further complicate the existing
mental problems. In a period of work with mental patients,
I had opportunity to observe the explosive violence of
voice sounds and sometimes of actions after prolonged silence.
When the patients could be induced to make any sort of voice
sound to break the silence and relieve the tension, violence
was unlikely.

Breathing patterns are of particular importance in the management
of schizophrenic children. I have observed that these
children are inclined to a restricted accessory breathing, which
contributes to an increase in the body tensions. Of those under
my surveillance, the most receptive hummed or made some
voice sound while engaged in activity. Even that slight release
of pressure was sufficient to alter their response to their environment.
The silent ones, I noted, went through intervals of
breath suspension and had no means of releasing tension-producing
pressures. Poor breathing patterns multiplied the
problems of the schizophrenic children by adding to their already
intolerable physical tensions and by reducing the oxygen
supply which their body, particularly the brain, so desperately
needed.

Poor breathing patterns can be calculated to manufacture
tensions and contribute further to existing difficulties. In
SIMBIC the establishment of breathing coordination results in

a sensation of complete relaxation, as the athletes experienced. The immediate general response to the release of tension is to talk freely. Some of the hard-topped tables I have used in the course of my instruction have proved to be a sort of dual psychiatrist's couch and confessional. Problems cause tensions and tensions cause problems. Release of tension is part of the solution to almost any problem. One pupil's entire problem was tension produced by physical factors in combination with overmedication. Psychiatric treatment and SIMBIC instruction were given simultaneously, and, to the amazement of everyone involved, the pupil upon relaxation was telling more to me than to the psychiatrist.

Tension has more bizarre effects upon the body than can be delineated. A suggestion of its potential was evident in the case of an internationally-known artist-philosopher who came to me at the suggestion of her physician for relief from the dyspnea of emphysema. A highly controversial figure in the art world, she had been subject to extreme mental pressures for a number of years, and as her physical condition grew worse, she despaired of being able to continue her creative work. When I met her, she had just come through a severe illness which very nearly ended her life, and she was a tangle of tensions. With SIMBIC she succeeded in releasing pressures she had come to accept as normal, and gradually she could resume her creative activities. A careful review of her case history revealed no immediate cause for the development of emphysema but did indicate that tension had contributed largely to the destruction of lung tissue and could very well have been the prime factor in the disease.

Corrosive effects of tension showed as surely in the athlete's performance as in the artist's ability to create. Accordingly, the Tahoe athletes were jubilant when they reached a given point in SIMBIC development and could release the tensions robbing them of their rest and plaguing them especially before competition. Used as part of the warm-up procedure, SIMBIC often presented the odd sight of a full-grown man stretched out on the grass chanting numbers to the sky. Strange conversations were also the order of the day.

"What do you think you're doing there, man? You sound like crazy," a new Tahoe arrival interrupted a SIMBIC veteran.

"I'm breathing, man, I'm breathing. It helps me run."

"Yeah?"

"Yeah."

"Where do you get this breathing stuff? Maybe I better have me some."

"See the Doc in the last trailer."

"Yeah?"

"Yeah."

In a day or so an unfamiliar face appeared in my doorway, and another SIMBIC pupil soon began shaking free of his devils and fiends.

17

TROUBLES IN SMALL PACKAGES

Perhaps because everything about Lake Tahoe is immense—the lake itself, the mountains, the trees, the desert to the east—I began to notice little things. Dusty little flowers bloomed by the roadside beneath gigantic pines. Small donkeys grazed contentedly in the meadow unaware of their measure against the great mountains. Inconspicuous brown rabbits nibbled in the thickets along shallow streams bearing presumptuous titles. Round and round the corral patient ponies plodded with their joyous young riders, to whom all the circumstances of the celebrated Olympics were no more than a good excuse for a glorious vacation.

Little things did not necessarily mean unimportant things. A few tiny rocks jarred out of place could bring a boulder crashing down the mountain. Those would-be cowboys clucking to their ponies had problems to match in importance any of those of a gold medal aspirant. Troubles bundled into small packages can often be more serious than the larger sizes. When I watched the children of the Olympic personnel and of the community and when I listened to their voices, I could detect the warning signs of respiratory problems. Neglected, as they undoubtedly would be through ignorance not lack of concern, the incipient problems could affect the entire lives of the chil-

dren and no one would ever know what really happened.

For over fifteen years hundreds of children from three years of age—some only two-and-a-half—to young adults have trooped past my piano at the Good Shepherd Choir School. I have observed their breathing and I have heard their voices. Some of their problems I have dealt with professionally as a respiratory consultant; others I have handled as best I could within the framework of the choirs; still others I have watched with sadness because I was not in a position to forestall the inevitable consequences of respiratory ignorance. So little is known about breathing that very little is done about it and very little attention is accorded it until too late.

Children, like athletes, are generally believed to breathe "naturally" unless they are obviously ill or prone to illness. Many children do retain the natural coordination of the normal, healthy infant well on into childhood, but far more lose it at an early age. When the natural coordination goes, the subsequent pattern is almost certain to exert undue stress on one or another of the muscles of breathing and effect a weakness. Such a weakness interferes with the efficient movement of air in and out the lungs and eventually results in some sort of respiratory complication.

Again like the athletes, children are especially susceptible to tensions. Tensions wreak havoc on small respiratory mechanisms, inflicting damage which can alter personalities and change the course of lives. A major portion of the tensions originate in the unrelenting competitiveness of contemporary society. Before a newborn infant can adjust to maintaining his body in the alien environment of earth, he begins to be urged to do something or other so that his parents can report a first. Growth and development, totally individualistic processes at an indeterminate pace, are transformed into competitive sports. From feeding to teething to toilet training, the infant is poked and prodded to hurry, hurry, hurry.

Little ones are encouraged to get to one goal so that they can rush on to the next. Time and accomplishment bring no letup in parental ambition for progress. Little systems rebel. Muscles tense and tighten. The sensitive respiratory system responds and trouble begins. A few colds may not seem to be important, but when they are followed by a few more, a fault in the breathing can almost certainly be suspected. Since the respiratory mechanism makes possible human functioning in earth's atmosphere, it is to be cherished, for without oxygen, the life expectation is reduced to, roughly, three minutes. No gratification of parental pride can possibly be worth the damages resulting from tensions, but most parents, unfortunately, are involved in their own problems and forget that troubles come in the small packages, too.

If a child survives the rigors of infancy unscathed, he numbers in the minority, for as early as three and four years the signs of tension begin to appear. When he is placed in the competitive situation of group activities, tensions mount with the pressures to equal and excel. As the inner turmoil increases, the pectoral muscles tend to tighten and raise the chest, thus putting the respiratory mechanism out of alignment and establishing a pattern of destructive accessory breathing. Should the condition persist, deterioration of the respiratory muscles and the attendant complications begin.

The warning signs of respiratory faults in otherwise healthy children are susceptibility to respiratory infections, the disappearance of the clear, bell-like quality normal to a child's voice, and some speech problems. The voice and the breathing are inseparable, and the alteration in the voice is nearly always matched by an alteration in the breathing. Sometimes the solution to the problem is as simple as relieving the pressures on the child; sometimes it is considerably more complicated.

When the most reliable member of my Cherub Choir, a self-possessed little lady of about five, started in kindergarten, her voice gradually lost its lovely clear quality, and the child herself began to lose her former amiability. Each week the changes became more noticeable and I corrected her breathing faults accordingly. Finally I spoke with her mother and learned that because of her vocal ability and enthusiasm she was being called upon to lead the singing of her class. Knowing the child, I suspected that in her excitement of group leadership she was singing not only for herself but for all the children. At my suggestion she was removed from her demanding position. With the release of that pressure both her voice and her disposition returned.

Many children develop the dangerous habit of holding the breath. Under tension they raise the shoulders in taking a breath and tense the muscles of the upper chest to hold it. Uncorrected, this habit will destroy any desirable pattern of breathing. When called upon in choir rehearsal to recite the words to a song, an unsure child frequently will hold his breath while trying to think. I can take care of the moment by telling him calmly just to relax and think, but I can do little about the other tensions in his life.

A deplorable destructive force which increasingly affects the child's voice and, subsequently, his breathing is the totally erroneous adult concept of a child's voice as being a high-pitched squeak or a growling monotone. The natural sound of the immature voice has a delicate, clear quality which no adult can imitate. To the gross adult ear, the higher pitch of the young voice may sound shrill and in adult imitations is interpreted as an unpleasant squeak, often nasal. Some misguided adults find these sounds highly amusing and encourage their children to duplicate them. Children, who are quick to imitate and placate adults, adopt the false voices of comic characters which have been made popular through recordings and television. The child not only alters his own voice but in producing the false sound, alters his breathing pattern. The cost of the adult amusement is the child's voice and respiratory health.

Because children are imitative, shrill unpleasant voices are often a reproduction of the unpleasant adult sounds they hear around them. In making the sounds breathing patterns have to be altered and candidacy for respiratory complaints is established. Adults sometimes think that a low-pitched growl is a manly sound for a little boy to make. Now, a low-pitched growl is not a manly sound nor is it a natural sound for a little boy to make. One young choir member had been urged by his parents to fit himself out with an unnatural, deep voice like his father and become a real rough-and tumble guy. He tried to please and every week I watched his chest grow tighter despite my intermittent efforts. I could succeed in getting him to relax his taut muscles and use his natural voice in singing, but I was not in a position to persuade his father to give up the unnatural speaking voice. Unhappily, I saw him develop into a nervous, irritable child.

With proper management of the breathing, the immature voice can be guided through the various stages of development without endangering the sound-producing structures in the throat. When the cherubs are brought to the Choir School, some at the age of two-and-a-half years, about seventy per cent of them would be counted as monotones. Unless they have a physical defect of ear or throat, a rare occurrence, they are monotones because their breathing is faulty or because their ear cannot yet distinguish pitch. By the age of six the proportion of monotones is reduced to five per cent, and by the age of eight they have all learned the proper production of sound and are singing. With guidance and constant supervision of the breathing, the voices of both the girls and the boys are brought through the difficult maturing process of adolescence without interruption of their careers in the choir. Two young girls who had exceptional voices began voice study at the ages of eight and twelve. Each matured gracefully, and one went on to do concert work in Europe while the other auditioned for the Metropolitan Opera and engaged in solo work during an interim of music study.

Both voice problems and respiratory health problems generally are rooted in faulty breathing. Without the necessary correction of the breathing, the problem will very likely go unsolved, as a choir member in his late teens learned from experience. He had had a series of minor illnesses which climaxed in a diagnosis of chronic bronchitis. No sooner did he recover from one illness than another began, and he lost so much time from school that his academic standing was jeopardized. Finally his parents consulted me about his breathing and its possible effect upon his respiratory condition. When I examined the young man, I found that his chest had tightened, forcing him into a pattern of accessory breathing. None of the medication given him was reaching the source of the infection. After two weeks of SIMBIC instruction the infection cleared. The correction of the breathing not only solved the respiratory problem, it also brought about a release of the tension which was a major contributing factor in the complexity.

Although the muscular resiliency of youth is a marvelous, built-in protective factor, the continual stress of faulty breathing and respiratory infection in combination with tensions will eventually destroy it. Children who cannot tolerate the unending tensions of growth and whose breathing has made them constant candidates for respiratory infection often seek refuge subconsciously in illness as a temporary relief from pressure. They have no other escape from the overpowering forces with which circumstance compels them to deal. The brief escape, however, does not remedy the situation.

The greatest single aid in the breathing problems of young children is to relieve the demanding pressures which cause a build-up of physical tensions likely to distort breathing patterns. The constant drive to achievement can do untold harm to the respiratory apparatus of the young. Early indications of approaching trouble are changes in voice quality and susceptibility to infections. Habits which will precipitate a pattern of accessory breathing and weaken the respiratory muscles are breath-holding and carrying the shoulders high rather than in a relaxed, lowered position. If the child's abdomen protrudes on speaking or exhaling in any fashion, the diaphragm is too weak to support the air pressure and ultimately may give rise to an assortment of respiratory complications. Because of muscular resiliency these symptoms of weakening of the muscles of breathing very often will disappear as the external pressures are relieved and the child can shed his tensions.

The little people grow to be big people, and as they grow, their troubles grow along with them. The respiratory ailments of childhood can cause injury which carries over into adult life and develops into respiratory disease and disorder of varying degrees of seriousness. Emphysema patients usually have long histories of respiratory infection. Many of the athletes had records of childhood respiratory complaints and many suffered the far-reaching consequences of early illnesses.

Correction of small troubles in the young can prevent much of the respiratory difficulty which neglect fosters in later life.

18

OUNCES AND POUNDS

During the first half of the intensive training and development program for the Olympic candidates in the application of SIMBIC to their individual needs, my thoughts and purposes underwent reorientation. In spite of all earnest effort and good intent the practice and competition conditions at the South Lake Tahoe High Altitude Study site did not match those which could be expected in Mexico City. None of the track meets held in the course of the summer had had any of the extreme tension and stress which the September finals for the selection of the Olympic team would have nor which the October games in Mexico City would have in even greater abundance. A practice competition and a determining competition are two different things.

Futhermore, Mexico City would have an air pollution factor absent from Tahoe. Coupled with the pressures of international competition for world championships, it could create breathing complications. I was becoming less and less interested in championships and more and more concerned with health and safety. I had observed the athletes enough to know that the champions extended themselves beyond the physical barriers and relied upon pure will for their victories. They could use the extra energy SIMBIC provided, but more than that, they, like all athletes, needed the means of preventing possible respiratory damage in their excessive exertion. I wanted to give them the ounces of prevention to avoid the necessity of pounds of cure long after the victories had become memories.

Because of the brief time allowed for the muscular development of breathing coordination, I questioned the ability of some of the men to withstand the grueling demands of final performance without supervision. I also had a particular concern for a number of the men who had had difficult recoveries at the several track meets during the summer and who could never get around to fulfilling their solemn vows to come for breathing instruction. SIMBIC was offered on a strictly volunteer basis because it requires self-discipline and is of minimum value unless continually applied. I hardly had time to see those who wanted it enough to come to be taught. I could not go seeking those whose resolution waned with the crisis, nor could I stop worrying about the consequences of their folly. They could have serious trouble without aid from someone thoroughly familiar with breathing processes and respiratory mechanics. Quite possibly that aid might not be available.

When the original plans for the SIMBIC instruction project were detailed, the work was to be conducted over the six weeks of the Medical Testing and Study program. If successful, it then would be considered for continuation through the games in Mexico City. The first track meet twelve days after the start of the program removed any lingering doubt of the effectiveness of SIMBIC or its value to the athlete. The first progress report brought an enthusiastic response from the Olympic Committee and the Tahoe staff. Everyone directly associated with the preparation for the Mexican games assumed that SIMBIC instruction and supervision would go on through the September finals until the games ended.

My approach to the matter was more realistic. I had no reservation about the importance of continuing through the games, but I knew that the financing of the project extension from the end of August on would be a major consideration for both the Olympic Committee and the Institute. I also knew that obtaining the credentials necessary to give me access to the team during their performance in Mexico City would be no simple matter. Even so, I addressed myself to the Olympic Committee Executive Board and advised as emphatically as I could that in the interest of health and safety the SIMBIC project be continued on the original terms. Then, according to my time-honored custom, I busied myself while waiting.

Staying busy was a rare problem at Tahoe, for someone was always drawn to my trailer door by sheer curiosity or by dire need. Nothing that materialized within the framework of the opening ever surprised me. I did not so much as blink twice the afternoon a small balding man with a bushy beard and eager eyes came to inquire about "some breathing lessons." He looked more like a prophet down off the mountain than an athlete, but he was in fact a walker from Israel who was working out at the track and felt that an improvement in his breathing would be advantageous. Since I was obligated to the U.S. Olympic Committee, I explained to him that in the interest of international harmony I would have to clear with Olympic officials. He nodded in understanding and ambled off into the forest silently as he had come. Later, when I was able to work with him, he became so enthusiastic that he wanted to export SIMBIC to Israel.

The Israeli athlete reminded me forcefully that everyone needs to learn how to manage his breathing. Although SIMBIC arose from the breathing needs of the chronically ill, its benefits to the well are manifold, particularly in prophylaxis—the prevention of trouble. Instinct has always prompted me to avoid complications which can be foreseen. My concern for the danger potential of the Tahoe finals and the Mexican games stemmed from this ounce-of-prevention-is-worth-a-pound-of-cure attitude, as did my steadily expanding interest in the application of SIMBIC to prophylaxis.

Work with the athletes had added to the Institute files quantities of material on the preventive values of SIMBIC and had underscored the relationship between breathing patterns and incidence of respiratory infection. Minor respiratory infections constantly recurring pave the way for later, more serious disorders. Whenever the number of such infections can be reduced, the likelihood of more complicated conditions developing in the future also is reduced. Prevention of respiratory problems with all their many ramifications is far better than any attempt to solve them.

Breathing by its very nature makes prophylaxis difficult. It is such an obvious human necessity that it generally is ignored until a problem calls attention to it. It requires little conscious effort and makes no direct demands on the individual for provision of a substance to be breathed. On the other hand, eating, also an obvious human necessity, is seldom neglected. It requires an amount of effort and makes unending demands on the individual for provision of an assortment of substances to be eaten. Not only is it a pleasure, it is a whole complex of industries and businesses. Much attention is given to the intake of appropriate quantities of proteins, fats, carbohydrates, vitamins, and minerals. Conversely, oxygen, the matter of breathing, occasions little notice, yet without the breathing of oxygen all the food could not be consumed.

Every function of the body requires oxygen. The act of breathing supplies oxygen for all cellular needs and removes the gaseous waste products of cellular activity. A constant turnover of air in the lungs is essential to the maintenance of good health. If oxygen is not supplied in appropriate quantity and carbon dioxide wastes are not removed effectively, the body will respond in a variety of seemingly unrelated ways, from drowsiness and headaches to tension, twinging muscles, and sneezes. Solely from the standpoint of physical comfort, breathing is worthy of consideration.

Consequences of faulty breathing can range from unpleasant to dangerous. Faulty breathing weakens the muscles of breathing, particularly those of exhale. As the muscles weaken, the turnover of air in the lungs decreases and residual volume increases, thus leaving an accumulation of gaseous waste products in the passageways of the lungs. In the "dead" spaces through which air is not circulated, infection settles just as scum settles on a pond through which no water flows freely. Circulation of the blood through the dead spaces tends to slow, and medication, regardless of quantity or quality, cannot act effectively upon the infection. In this manner the groundwork is laid for a cycle of recurrent illnesses which in their own good time can damage the lungs and create a respiratory cripple.

SIMBIC has been particularly efficient in breaking down the cycle of illnesses and preventing recurrence. The prophylaxis study at St. Albans indicated the value of SIMBIC in reducing the incidence of pneumonia. Because of the existing sensitivity of the lungs, respiratory patients are constantly in danger of contracting an infection which develops into pneumonia. Lung damage from prior illnesses leaves dead spots within the lungs, and conventional medication procedures fail to clear the infection in these spots. All too frequently another pneumonia follows. A patient in the St. Albans study had had three pneumonia illnesses within one year before he began SIMBIC instruction. After he developed his breathing coordination, he went for the remainder of my stay at the hospital, two years or so, without another occurrence of pneumonia. Others in the study who had case histories of repeated infections had no infections during that time.

By effectual movement of air through the lungs SIMBIC opens the dead spots, stimulates the blood circulation, and enables the medication to act upon the infection. An emphysema patient who had been hospitalized for six weeks in an attempt to diagnose and treat an infection of steadily increasing seriousness came to me for a long-overdue SIMBIC checkup. We corrected some faults he had developed in his absence, then he went back to the hospital for additional medication. With the opening of the dead spots the medication could take effect, and after a few days the stubborn infection cleared. As long as the breathing is correct, SIMBIC pupils who have emphysema can clear infections in a matter of days even though they may have histories of extended, serious illnesses.

The athletes at Tahoe were akin to the emphysema patients in that the severe demands upon their respiratory system made them susceptible to colds and respiratory infections. Tahoe had a bouncing thermometer which rose and set with the sun, and the athletes were constantly overheating and cooling their bodies. The chill, dusty mountain air was conducive to colds of all sorts. However, the men in the SIMBIC project had fewer colds and colds of shorter duration than those outside the project. One runner incurred a serious respiratory infection when he left Tahoe for a weekend to participate in a track meet. He asked for an extra SIMBIC session, and his infection cleared in record time. Infections not only tend to damage the athlete's respiratory mechanism, they drain his body's energy and reduce his performance potential. The more quickly they are cleared, the less likely they are to cause lasting effects.

An athlete's respiratory mechanism is as much a part of his physical equipment for performance as the body structures directly employed in performance. His muscles of breathing sustain the total organism and require proper development for maximum efficiency. Every athletic program, whether for Little Leaguers or world champions, could make an appreciable contribution to the health and safety of its participants by including thorough respiratory instruction. Proper respiratory management reduces the probability of damage from faulty breathing under stress and promotes general health through a stimulation of the circulatory system. It eliminates many physical problems before they ever have an opportunity to take root and flourish.

Similarly, effective respiratory programs incorporated into the school curriculum would provide special advantages for children and young people. Proper breathing, as the athletes discovered, induces a state of relaxation and prevents the build-up of corrosive tensions. Pupils and teachers alike could do very well with a reduction in classroom tension. Even more important is the maintenance of a steady oxygen supply to the body with the accompanying benefits in health and well-being. Young people who want to "turn on" and experience fully the sensations of the physical being will find that the positive stimulation of a naturally well-oxygenated system sustained by proper breathing is far more satisfying than the negative stimulation of drugs and chemical products.

Because human beings live in the atmosphere and must derive their very source of life and energy—oxygen—from the atmosphere, their respiratory system and its employment are of supreme importance to them whether or not they choose to recognize and respect the fact. Proper breathing can avoid or reduce the consequences of many of the evils flesh is heir to; improper breathing can and does affect the other systems of the body detrimentally. With the unceasing pollution of the environment, proper breathing becomes the most potent form of health insurance. In urban areas of concentrated air pollution, knowing how to breathe for maximum efficiency amounts to possession of a weapon for survival.

Air pollution combined with tensions, which are at the base of most of the major problems of mechanized, commercialized society, creates a critical need for the ounces of prevention, particularly when they are as simple as proper breathing. The pounds of cure often prove to be too little come too late.

19

HALF A LOAF

From time to time the athletes came to me about "this friend in L.A.," or Denver, or Kansas City, or some other distant point, who "needs a little help with breathing. What'll I tell him?" The question seemed so innocent that only a stock reply should have been required, but I never could bring myself to develop an automatic response. I have always worked with individuals and individual problems. Knowing the intricacies of breathing and the differences between people, I hesitate to give general advice. What can be helpful to one can just as readily be harmful to another.

SIMBIC is concerned with the involuntary muscles of breathing, their tone, and their development. It has nothing to do with any form of calisthenics designed to force the operation of these muscles through use of the voluntary muscles or external pressures. Despite the radical nature of the entire concept of breathing coordination, the acceptance of SIMBIC as a complete departure from all previous approaches to the act of breathing seems to be extremely difficult for both the scientist and the layman. When an attempt is made to simplify the subject, the response is all too often the automatic assumption that this is just a new presentation of an old topic, one already long since exhausted. The topic is indeed old, but accurate, scientific knowledge of it is only at a beginning. Most popular notions of it amount to folklore.

Many people who have had singing lessons or who have practiced "belly-breathing" or yoga are firmly convinced that they know the major facts of breathing, yet time and again I have been called upon to redevelop the abused and weakened diaphragms of just such people. As the wise man remarked, "It isn't what people know that hurts them. It's what they think they know that isn't so." What most people think they know about breathing simply is not so.

A very real need for respiratory education exists. All the friends in L.A. and Denver and Kansas City should be told enough about the management of breathing to enable them to use their respiratory equipment intelligently and avoid the common distresses of the day. SIMBIC, however, by virtue of dealing with the singularity of the individual's respiratory structure, cannot be reduced to a do-it-yourself formula. Dr. Nims of West Haven has tried unsuccessfully for more than five years to analyze and define SIMBIC in terms which any medical man can follow to achieve the desired result of establishing breathing coordination. Time and research lie between the knowledge of the existence of breathing coordination and its availability to the public.

Meanwhile, the benefits of proper breathing habits are so numerous and the need for knowledge and practice of proper breathing is so great that half a loaf would appear to be better than none. Whatever advice I could give the athletes to pass on to their friends might possibly be better than their having no instruction at all. When I agreed to tell the men "what to tell 'em," I also warned that they were giving not SIMBIC instruction but general advice on breathing. I noted further that the advice was for the well. Anyone with a serious respiratory problem or disease should be exceedingly cautious about following general advice intended for the well. Where damage already is present, the possibility of further damage also is present.

Acutely aware of the pitfalls of oversimplification, I proceeded to advise. My experience has been that most people have a somewhat vague idea of the respiratory mechanism, its structure, and its functions. This deficit in the departments of anatomy and physiology creates some rather curious notions about the process of breathing. Observation of the external motions of the body during the act of breathing can be very misleading about what is going on inside. Knowledge is not necessary to the performance of the act, but it does help to clear away some of the misconceptions.

First of all, the body has to come off the flattened textbook pages and be thought of as a kind of cylinder which, in breathing, functions all the way around, not just in front, as it would often seem to. The lungs lie within the encompassing cage of the ribs like two inverted cones with the base toward the mid-region of the body. They should be filled with air from the bottom to the top, just as any container is filled. The lungs, however, are not just any container. They possess the peculiar property of being able to be filled partially from the top, and herein is the origin of numberless respiratory problems. Accessory breathing, as this partial filling from the top is called, destroys the natural breathing pattern, alters the position of the chest, weakens the muscles of breathing, and makes the practitioner a prime candidate for various respiratory infections and disabilities.

Proper breathing always fills the lungs from the base at the middle of the body, and the action of breathing occurs principally in this middle area. The entire circumference of the mid-region should contract and expand with the movement of air out and in the lungs. Back motion in breathing generally is neglected, but it is of vital importance. When the back muscles are inoperative, accessory breathing begins. The athletes used the sensation of the back motion to maintain breathing coordination during performance. When the back tensed, they went into accessory breathing, and their efficiency was reduced immediately.

Breathing motion at the middle of the body does not mean that the diaphragm is moving in and out, as many believe. The motion is due to the emptying and filling of the lungs. In the process of breathing, the diaphragm, which extends through the center of the body from back to front separating the chest cavity from the abdominal cavity, moves upward on the exhale and downward on the inhale like a flexible dome. The upward movement helps to move air out of the lungs; the downward movement results from the pressure of the incoming air. With the movement of the diaphragm is a corresponding movement in the abdominal region. Diaphragmatic motion downward increases the pressure within the abdominal cavity and causes the abdomen to move outward. Upward motion of the diaphragm decreases that pressure and the abdomen tends to flatten. The abdominal muscle supports the diaphragm but never forces it.

The motion of the abdomen in the breathing process should not be confused with the form of breathing known as "belly-breathing," which employs the abdominal muscle to force the motion of the diaphragm. In the case of a weakened diaphragm such forcing causes further damage and can produce numerous respiratory complications. "Belly-breathing" also tends to force the ribs upward and outward on the exhale and can alter the position of the chest.

Contrary to general belief, the more important phase of breathing is the exhale, the movement of air from the lungs. If a container is to be refilled, it must first be emptied of its contents. The lungs are containers for the body's supply of air with life-giving oxygen. Before they can be refilled with a new supply, they must be emptied of their waste-containing old supply. The sensation of breathlessness does not indicate, as is often supposed, the need to fill the lungs. It indicates instead the need to empty the lungs so that they can be re-filled. Attempts to introduce more air into already overinflated lungs increases the sensation of breathlessness. When air has been removed in sufficient quantity on the exhale, the auto-matic inhale occurs and the body needs for oxygen can be satisfied.

A natural device for promoting a long, relaxed exhale is the sigh. The aftermath of the sigh is an intake of air. Sighs gen-erally follow a period during which breathing has become slow and needs to be increased. The long, relaxed exhale, which is the principle of the sigh, can be cultivated to advantage. Like the sigh itself, it should be a product of muscular tone, never of force. Counting silently often helps to prolong the exhale.

Too much cannot be said against the use of any form of force, muscular or mechanical, to compel the operation of the muscles of breathing. Breathing is a relaxed process. When it becomes forced, the desirable pattern is destroyed and undue stress falls upon individual muscles. With the destruction of the original pattern, an altered pattern of accessory breathing is adopted and, if continued, can weaken the respiratory apparatus.

When the long, relaxed exhale has been mastered, a person

with no respiratory problems can improve the tone of his muscles of breathing by adding sound to the exhale and counting aloud. Anyone with a serious respiratory problem should be guided through the muscular redevelopment process and would be very wise to confine himself to the long, silent exhale. Production of sound places more stress upon the muscles than the ill can support.

The well should begin with a low count of ten and continue a relaxed exhale at the end of the audible count. After the subsequent inhale the count should be increased by five and the exhale extended as before. With gradual rise, by fives, in the count the inhale following will tend to increase and each exhale to lengthen. If the lower abdomen begins to tense or forcing occurs, counting must stop. Performed correctly, the procedure gives a sensation of total relaxation. The general high count on a single breath is about one hundred and times to fifteen to twenty seconds. After the muscles have developed, the high count may average thirty or forty seconds on a single breath.

Counting should be conducted in a supine position. The floor will do nicely and will eliminate the need for expensive equipment. The body should remain relaxed throughout the procedure, for breathing is a relaxed process and induces relaxation. Any forcing of the count or tensing of the rib cage indicates a fault and should be avoided. The inhale should always be a spontaneous response to the prolonged, relaxed exhale at the end of the oral count. The shoulders should be kept down and the chest relaxed. If the lower abdomen protrudes on the count, a weakened diaphragm is indicated and the count should be suspended. In such event a return to silent counting in a prolonged exhale is advisable. To continue the application of sound would weaken the dia-

208

phragm further and cancel any benefits to be derived from the process.

Breathing is a rhythmical function which requires constant maintenance to keep the body supplied with oxygen for efficient operation. Often in periods of concentration or tension the tendency is to hold or suspend the breath. Such a habit of breath-holding can be detrimental to the body and can produce bizarre results. A doctor with whom I was associated had reached a point at which he was seriously considering giving up operation of his car. He had begun to experience "blackouts" while driving and had almost incurred several serious accidents. At one time we had discussed the diminished supply of oxygen to the brain brought about by breath-holding, and he happened to remember the discussion. Upon observation he discovered that in the tensions of traffic he held his breath. When he maintained his breathing, the blackouts ceased.

Students and persons engaged in mental activity are inclined to hold or to slow the breath when they concentrate. The reduced supply of oxygen to the brain reflects in sluggishness and sleepiness and in a healthy respiratory mechanism will cause a yawn. For peak mental efficiency, attention should be given to the breathing and a rhythmical pattern should be maintained.

Rhythmical breathing is not to be interpreted as "systematic breathing"; that is, a certain count for the exhale and a certain count for the inhale. The only thing to be said for the practice is that it avoids breath-holding. Such a system of breathing destroys natural breathing patterns and sets up artificially maintained patterns in place. The artificial patterns cannot accommodate the constantly changing needs of the body and will produce numerous ill effects. A well-known athlete with whom I worked briefly employed systematic breathing. He had a weakened diaphragm and suffered constantly from abdominal pressure pains and side stitches during performance. He also had a serious stomach-ulcer condition caused by the innumerable pressures and tensions of top-level competition. Although he was aware of his physical improvement with SIMBIC, he could not bring himself to abandon his former habits and accept SIMBIC discipline. Through the season his condition gradually deteriorated, and he eventually lost his national standing.

Since the diaphragmatic muscle not only participates in breathing but also regulates the pressure in the thoracic and abdominal cavities, abdominal conditions affect the breathing. Any undue pressure in the lower abdomen, such as that caused by overeating or by pregnancy, restricts the breathing. The abdominal muscle was designed to support, not force, but support the diaphragm. When the abdominal muscle weakens and permits the viscera to sag, an abnormal descent of the diaphragm occurs. Unless the condition is corrected, diaphragmatic weakness will result.

The abdominal muscle can be strengthened for its supporting role through the practice of simple leg-lifting exercises. In the supine position the legs should be lifted alternately a comfortable number of times then raised together if possible. The exercise should never be carried to the point of strain. Overexertion is never wise.

Breathing is a process which will occur of itself, but proper breathing requires considerably more attention. Improved breathing for health and efficiency in the oxygen-starved state of modern society is an undertaking well worth intelligent pursuit.

20

A SWING
OF THE PENDULUM

Time at Tahoe was a relentless enemy steadily advancing. Runners ran against the clock and everyone raced the calendar. So much had to be accomplished before the September finals that no day could be stretched enough to include everything. Each swing of the pendulum reminded me of some task left undone. At one extreme of the arc were the breathing problems of the Olympic candidates; at the other were those of emphysema patients in the East from whom by now I had been too long absent. As the pendulum swung from *tic* to *toc*, I knew that I had to duplicate the action and betake myself from West to East on a hurried journey to attend some urgent matters.

My opportunity came when the athletes had to leave Tahoe for a few days to participate in competitions "down below." I winged my way back to New York and plunged into a schedule marvelously planned to include everything except sleep. Part of my mission had to do with the Tahoe finals. The other part was devoted to Institute business and to affairs concerning the work in emphysema. The *tic* of the clock was deafening.

All the emphysematous SIMBIC pupils had weathered the

211

summer well and were eager for reports from the mountains. As I checked them to make certain that they had not fallen into breathing faults, a curious phenomenon occurred. I had the strange feeling that I was viewing the athletes through a magnifying glass. Apart from the condition of the lungs, the difference between the extremes was primarily one of degree. The small problems of breathing in the athletes were exaggerated into major difficulties in the emphysema patient. The dyspnea of the athlete's recovery period became a common experience of the patient. Both suffered similar apprehensions and dangers, but to the former these were the norm of competition while to the latter they were a way of life. Breathlessness, regardless of the immediate cause, always has the same fundamental cause.

Prior to SIMBIC, the overinflated condition of the lungs which produced breathlessness in the emphysema patient was understood, but the reason for the persistence of the condition was not. The alveoli, or air cells of the lungs, lost their elasticity because of some form of damage and served as traps to hold within the lungs air which normally should have been moved out on the exhale. On the subsequent inhale the trapped air blocked the intake of necessary quantities of new air, and the body's requirement for oxygen set off the sensation of breathlessness. That was all clear enough. What was not clear was the underlying reason for the failure of untrapped air to be moved out efficiently on the exhale. The obvious reason for dyspnea, the air trapping in the alveoli due to the cells' loss of elasticity, did not explain the condition completely.

The research work in SIMBIC revealed that the loss of cellular elasticity was a secondary cause of dyspnea. The primary cause was the breakdown of the mechanics of breathing. Reasons for the weakening of the muscles of breathing were

212

many; the results were the same: breathlessness. The weakened muscles were unable to move out untrapped air efficiently and to open new areas of the lungs for the effective exchange of gases. Through SIMBIC the individual pattern of muscular co-ordination could be reestablished and the weakened muscles could be redeveloped to move air from and into the lungs at peak efficiency with minimum effort and without the employment of any of the artificial devices which have been developed to aid the breathing. A radical aspect of SIMBIC is that redevelopment of the involuntary muscles was not considered to be possible.

Obviously, SIMBIC could not restore the damaged lung tissue, but with the redevelopment of the weakened muscles and the restoration of the proper mechanics of breathing, it made possible the employment of previously inactive lung areas at the highest level of efficiency of which the individual was capable. The deterioration of the tissue through the stress of exertion was halted and the progress of the disease was arrested. An advanced patient who had adhered to SIMBIC discipline faithfully was in better physical condition five years after he began to practice SIMBIC than he was at the outset. His respiratory functions were improved and his general health was far superior. When he began, he had been taking oxygen daily of necessity. He immediately eliminated the oxygen and never returned to it. He has completely incorporated SIMBIC into his pattern of living and constantly attends his muscular development.

The dyspnea of the athletes and the dyspnea of the emphysema patient differ only in that the athletes do not have a breakdown of lung tissue. However, the overinflation of the lungs with unexpelled air is the same and the breakdown of the mechanics of breathing is the same. The photographs of the emphysema patient which I had tacked to the wall of my trailer served to remind the athletes of the dangers inherent in poor breathing management. Similarly, the athletes were a symbol of the physical discipline required of the patient in his maintenance of his breathing coordination.

Effects of dyspnea on the athlete are principally of the moment; whereas, the effects on the emphysema patient are pervasive, exerting their influence long after the immediate emergency. Because the breathing affects all the functions of the body, the nervous system responds to breathlessness by producing tensions and causing unstable emotions. In the well the state passes with relative speed; in the diseased it lingers and lowers the individual's tolerance to situations he might have endured at one time. When this tendency is unknown to the patient's family and associates, he is considered disagreeable and difficult and is subject to a lack of understanding which can upset him and lead back into an attack of dyspnea.

The interrelationship of the breathing and the nervous system makes most of the emphysema patient's responses an exaggeration of the normal response. The patient's nerves are frayed by his constant preoccupation with his breathing and an incident of minor consequence can bring about dyspnea. I have observed a patient in the simple process of trying to arrange a luncheon appointment with an acquaintance become so involved that he was out of breath at the end. Another who conducts important business transactions on the telephone can become unduly disturbed by failure to complete a call. Tension can result from a minor occurrence as readily as from a major and can just as readily produce dyspnea. No buffering emotional reserve is available.

Tensions and pressures can damage the respiratory system as effectively as infection and disease and result in emphysema. For the most part, the emphysematous tend to be intense people who pursue their interests immoderately. Their very nature makes them candidates for the disease. Once they have developed the condition, they have difficulty in modifying their activities to live with it comfortably. Having no visible signs of disability, they often cannot accept the fact that they will not return to a former state of health. When they feel good, they overexert and exhaust themselves. Since they lack physical reserve, they require considerably longer than normal for recovery. They also are inclined to disguise their true state of health and pretend in public to be far fitter than they are. The pretense does double disservice. They overextend themselves, and their public activity deceives their private associates, who find the invisible illness hard to believe. Lack of sympathy on the part of associates is the gray ghost constantly haunting the emphysema patient, who never seems to be quite able to elicit understanding.

According to individual physical state, the person with emphysema is like an automobile with a given quantity of gas in the tank. How the gas is used is of little consequence, whether in a long trip or in traffic or in leakage. When it is gone, it is gone, and no matter how much mileage is left in the engine, the car will not move without more gas. The emphysematous has a given quantity of body energy. Whether he uses it in physical activity, mental activity, or nervous waste does not matter. When it is gone, he will have to stop and recover. His recovery is slower than normal because the disease is constantly draining away a portion of energy.

Warning against overexertion should not be taken as advice to become inactive. Inactivity slows the body processes and can cause highly undesirable states of congestion. In undertaking physical activity the emphysematous should be very cautious of exercises. Physical exercises may give a passing sense of well-being because they tend to increase the circulation; however, the extra strain imposed by increased breathing demands of exercise upon already weakened muscles of breathing offsets the temporary benefit. The patient has to know himself well enough to gear his activity to his available energy.

To aid his breathing, he should keep in mind always that his problem is to move air from the lungs. Again, any advice on breathing procedure should be followed with utmost caution because the breathing mechanism is weakened and is liable to further damage. With care the patient can learn to prolong the exhale. In the beginning the air should be expelled from the lungs to a silent count of five with no forcing of any sort. The lips should be separated to allow free passage of air. Pursed lips are likely to offer more resistance than the breathing muscles can support. They can also cause the bronchial tubes to swell and constrict the air passages. The upper chest remains relaxed, with shoulders down, and the lower abdomen must not protrude on the exhale. The breathing motion comes from the circumference of the mid-region of the body, and care is necessary to avoid tensing the rib cage. This procedure should be followed in as nearly a supine position as the patient can tolerate. If necessary, he can elevate head and shoulders with pillows, but the torso should be straight.

The silent count can be increased gradually by two's or five's as the patient observes all the attendant conditions of relaxation and is careful to avoid protrusion of the lower abdomen. If the abdominal muscle is weakened, the leg-lifting exercise can be undertaken with care not to overexert or strain. As the prolonged exhale is mastered, the inhale will occur spontaneously and may become deeper. The patient should keep his breathing constantly in mind and should be aware that change in body activity and body position will alter the supine pattern of breathing. He must remember that the breathing action occurs in the midregion of the body and that the back is included in the motion. The body is never made to function by application of muscular force. Thinking the action will cause it to happen through the body's own processes. Breathing is always relaxed.

Any patient who decides to undertake the oral count suggested for the well should do so in full knowledge that the addition of voice to the breathing places as much strain upon the muscles of breathing as physical exertion. He should proceed slowly, observing all the precautions of the silent count. The moment the natural voice alters or the abdomen protrudes, he should stop. Protrusion of the abdomen indicates the inability of the diaphragm to support the air pressure. Again, the breathing must not be forced by constriction of either the abdomen or upper chest and throat.

Certain breathing procedures can be helpful to the emphysema patient in his daily activities. Possibly the most demanding task he is called upon to perform is climbing stairs. He should keep in mind that he is moving his body against gravity and that the movement of dead weight is doubly difficult. Although the breathing procedure would seem to counter reason, it is the reverse of normal because the slow inhale is very difficult for the untrained, as is change of diaphragmatic motion. Both tend to induce breath-holding, which is detrimental under any conditions and particularly so under conditions of exertion. The climb, then, begins with an inhale and continues upward on a long exhale, with the body leaning slightly forward to take advantage of the momentum. The patient should proceed as far as possible comfortably, pause

217

for the automatic inhale, and go forward on the exhale. The body should always move forward. Hauling of dead weight from step to step is far more exhausting than continuing in motion.

For the performance of tasks an exhale when the body bends and an inhale when the body straightens make the chores easier. An exhale helps in sitting or stooping; an inhale aids rising. The exhale for bending the body eliminates air pressure against which the muscles otherwise would have to work with an unnecessary expenditure of energy. The most important point is to avoid holding the breath. Concentration is on the motion of the back and the maintenance of breathing.

Emphysema patients do well to eat moderately. Large quantities of food in the stomach increase the pressure in the abdomen and restrict movement of the diaphragm, thereby making breathing difficult. Food should be taken in small quantities with increased frequency. If a patient suffers a loss of appetite, he can supplement his diet with a nutriment to prevent undue weight loss. Like food, sleep or rest is also more beneficial in small quantities than over an extended time.

Self-medication is a practice which often produces undesirable results. If a little medication helps, more medication will not necessarily help more, as some misguided patients seem to think. Overmedication can cause tensions and nervousness which increase the breathing problem and effect a physical condition worse than that originally requiring medication.

As must the athlete, the emphysema patient has to learn to adapt his activities and his physical habits to achieve his prime objective. For the athlete, that objective is top performance in competition. For the patient, it is top performance within the restrictions of his disease.

218

21

THE MASTER SWITCH

My return to Tahoe from my flight to the East was memorable for the mound of mail awaiting. The past had caught up with me. From the start, press coverage of activities at the Olympic high altitude study site had been plentiful, and sɪᴍʙɪᴄ had received a colorful share. The resulting reader-correspondence stirred up had accumulated during my brief absence and stood ready to fill my idle hours. The range of inquiries was as broad as the mountains themselves. Everyone seemed to have a problem in some fashion involving breathing.

Emphysema patients, as might be expected, were numerous, as were aspiring athletes who longed for a formula to give them what nature had denied. All manner of respiratory sufferers sought relief from their distress; people with nervous disorders wanted to know whether breathing would help; and heart patients who had experienced shortness of breath were interested. A group of entertainers who had run out of breath during a high altitude engagement were concerned for their next trip to the mountains. The Olympic candidates had turned breathing into the most popular of the year-round sports. Naturally, I approved of that. Breathing is a very good thing to do.

While the interest in SIMBIC pleased me on one hand, it distressed me on the other. I was pleased that people were becoming more aware of the importance of breathing habits. I was distressed by the indication of the multiplicity of breathing problems. With every enlargement of my contact with the public I saw more clearly that the failure to recognize and accept the extreme importance of the act of breathing was a fatal error on the part of mankind.

The respiratory system with its vital function of breathing is a sort of master switch for the entire body. It turns on the body activities at birth and turns them off at death. It supplies the body with the oxygen necessary for the maintenance of life. As the supplier of life-giving oxygen, breathing affects the entire body. When the synergistic pattern of breathing coordination breaks down, the results are sometimes obvious, as in the case of respiratory disease and disorder. More often, they are subtle, disturbing some other system of the body with no visible indication that respiration could be involved even remotely. Because breathing is vital, sundry devices have been provided to maintain it and to keep the body operative. With the breakdown of breathing coordination, accessory breathing takes over and the individual himself is none the wiser. He may suffer the consequences the remainder of his life and never know that the real cause of his trouble is the way he breathes.

Quite obviously, a respiratory disease or disorder can be expected to respond to an increase in breathing efficiency. The degree of severity of respiratory complaints is determined by the degree of weakness of the muscles of breathing. If those muscles are not capable of moving air out and in the lungs efficiently, the remaining air will establish conditions conducive to infection and will cause dead spaces into which infection will settle beyond the reach of medication.

Often, emphysema patients who come to me for a checkup will comment that they have not been feeling as good as usual, and in the course of the session a telltale bit of mucus will indicate an unsuspected infection. Mild medication and careful attention to breathing will clear the condition in a day or so. Where a more serious infection exists, appropriate medication and proper breathing management prevent the development of a major illness. But, no amount of medication can be fully effective unless it is moving into the areas of the infection. The breathing does the moving.

In addition to emphysema SIMBIC has been effective in the management of asthma, bronchitis, pneumonia, bronchiectasis, and various respiratory infections. Wherever a breathing problem exists, a breakdown in the mechanics of breathing is sure to exist also. Scar tissue from tuberculosis, pneumonia, and respiratory infections frequently causes labored breathing. An artist, a brilliant woman and wife of a distinguished scientist, had extensive scar tissue from tuberculosis and had sought relief from breathing difficulties in both this country and Europe. She was advised repeatedly that unimpeded movement of air through her lungs was impossible. With SIMBIC she experienced unlabored breathing for the first time in years. The coordination and development of her muscles of breathing made possible the movement of air through the unaffected lung areas, thus enabling her to use to maximum efficiency the lung tissue available for exchange of gases.

A somewhat similar condition brought a very gracious lady, wife of an Olympic official, to me at Tahoe. She had a long history of respiratory infections and tuberculosis complicated by other conditions. She did not want her busy, active life disrupted by breathlessness and was ready to undertake SIMBIC discipline with the purposefulness of a gold medal contender. She made excellent progress and learned to manage her breathing to meet her needs.

Since breathing is the master switch of the body, the diversity of its effects and applications never surprised me. During the long, careful years of research, so many indications of SIMBIC potential appeared and so many were applied successfully that I did not doubt the efficacy of breathing coordination no matter how remote the possibility might seem. The relaxing effect on the nervous system alone relieved a multitude of evils. More important, I knew that the restoration of the muscles of breathing to their proper functioning could in no way inflict damage upon the body. If any question arose, it was how much, not whether, SIMBIC could be of direct value.

The question arose on a bright, crisp afternoon toward the end of August when the athletes were preparing to go "down below" again for competitions and I was planning to stay "upstairs" to sort a backlog of data. I came down from my trailer into the communications center to the information that a man from Laguna Beach was looking for me. I left a schedule of my whereabouts for the remainder of the day and went about my business. After a reasonable passage of time he found me. He had read of the Tahoe SIMBIC project in the Los Angeles papers and, on the slender chance that I might be able to help or advise him, had made the long automobile trek from Laguna to Tahoe to discuss his problem.

Thin, earnest, middle-aged, fatigued by his unbroken journey, he was in search of nothing more than hope for his grandson. The boy, age ten, suffered chronic refractory heart failure due to a severe pulmonary vascular disease and was

222

living on borrowed time. Doctors had completely discouraged hope, which was all the man wanted—just a shred of hope that the child might survive. He believed implicitly that an improvement in breathing would help, and he was right, but breathing could not alter the existing physical condition.

As best I could, I explained that the benefits of SIMBIC would be of a general nature and of indeterminate direct value to the child's heart ailment. In conscience, I could not permit him to believe that this was the miracle he secretly pursued. Nevertheless, he was determined to explore every possibility and urged me to return to Laguna Beach with him that evening. I could not comply, but I did agree to fly down over the weekend to work with the boy. I was not certain to what extent SIMBIC would help, but I knew that it would give the grandfather the immeasurable satisfaction of having tried.

Upon my arrival I found a bright-eyed, handsome little boy who readily learned the fundamentals of SIMBIC and who gave few indications of the gravity of his condition. I instructed all members of the household so that they might be able to help the boy attend his breathing and derive maximum benefit from it. In that time and a subsequent period I spent with him, his breathing improved appreciably and affected favorably some of the debilitating complications of the heart condition. SIMBIC could not offer him a blank check to draw on life, but it did provide extra credits for the borrowing of more time. How much time he could continue to borrow was not predictable, but he escaped the immediate threat to his life and gave his grandfather the hope sought.

Chief value of SIMBIC in the management of heart disease is the easy movement of air through the lungs to provide more oxygen for the body and relieve some of the strain on the heart. Emphysema patients tend to have a secondary heart condition due to the demands made upon the heart by the effort of breathing. Notations of the effect of improved breathing on the circulatory system were as early as the work in East Orange and continued through the entire SIMBIC research. Particularly at West Haven immediate improvement in heart condition appeared after SIMBIC sessions. Sufficient evidence exists to warrant the theory that a breakdown in the mechanics of breathing can impose severe enough strain on the heart to cause heart failure.

Just as breathing affects the heart, the heart can affect the breathing with its increased oxygen requirements. The same is true of the nervous system. All the systems of the body are a two-way exchange with the repercussions of disorder in one being reflected in the disturbance of the other. The nervous system is highly responsive to the breathing, and vice versa. SIMBIC has caused numerous unusual side effects because of the interrelationship of the systems of the body. Among the athletes at Tahoe the sleeplessness resulting from body tensions was relieved with the improvement in the breathing and the relaxation accompanying the establishment of breathing coordination. No one could have been more surprised than they to discover that their manner of breathing helped them sleep. Emphysema patients who had not slept for several nights often fell asleep during SIMBIC sessions.

In the Boys' Club study prior to the Olympics project a novel response to SIMBIC occurred. A seventeen-year-old boxer who had just completed a series of bouts to win the Golden Gloves championship faced two challengers. At the time he was considered "overtrained" and his coach was concerned because of the impending competition. A sensitive young man disposed to various tensions, he had extreme body tension with chest raised and tensed so that the pectoral muscles were hardened. He frequently laughed uncontrollably and for some time he had lacked his usual body coordination. When SIMBIC instruction began, his diaphragm went into a spasm and he could not stop laughing. As he began to relax, the laughter ceased but the leg and body muscles quivered out of control for several minutes. By the end of the session he could breathe in a coordinated pattern.

At the second session he became completely relaxed and the tension disappeared. By the third session a speech defect due to weakened respiratory muscles had improved noticeably and he was recovering more quickly between boxing rounds. Meanwhile, he came in first in the marathon with the report that he had no problem. As the breathing developed, the jerkiness of his movements vanished and he went on to win his challenge fights, which he termed the "easiest fighting" he had ever done. What had appeared to be "overtraining" was actually muscular tension caused by the emotional tension of the impending series of competitions. Faulty breathing had forged an endless chain of destructive tensions and fatigue which threatened the young man's health as well as his athletic achievements. No one even suspected the real cause of the trouble.

Similarly, speakers and singers and persons called upon to use the voice a great deal often experience a form of laryngitis derived from throat fatigue and tensions. The real cause of the condition is faulty breathing. When the mechanics of breathing are impaired, the respiratory muscles cannot support the stress of voice production, and throat tensions result from the efforts to force the voice. Body fatigue imposes extra stress upon the muscles of breathing. Uncommon demands made on the respiratory system during periods of fatigue can very well cause voice difficulties.

Another condition, this one seemingly remote from breathing, which has made a surprising response to SIMBIC is stomach ulcers. An emphysema patient who had had ulcers for an extended time noticed that his condition improved as his breathing improved. Finally, the ulcers disappeared altogether and he has not since—a matter of several years—had a recurrence. Other SIMBIC pupils have paralleled the experience. The implications are that the relief of tension brought about by breathing coordination served to ease the tension-controlled factors underlying the ulcer condition.

Among the rainbow assortment of SIMBIC surprises at Tahoe was the correction of chronic sore back problems. One athlete, a decathlon man and a medical doctor, had had a chronic sore back for four months prior to coming to Tahoe. On maximum exertion he went into accessory breathing and had difficulty in recovering. When his breathing coordination had been established and the muscles began to develop, he was able to take harder workouts than he had at sea level and for the first time he had no recovery problem. In running, his weakest event, he broke his life record. Added to all of that, the sore back cleared. A coach who had SIMBIC instruction found that the relaxation resulting eased his tensions and relieved a back condition due to bone growth. He reported jubilantly that for the first time in thirteen years he had no back pain. With removal of tension all kinds of things happen.

Another athlete was sent to me because he had incurred an oxygen debt during workout and had blacked out. Subsequently, he developed the dreaded kidney condition which often results from an oxygen debt. However, the increased oxygen supply available to him through the improvement in breathing enabled him to recover from the kidney infection in three days. Later he maintained a daily workout schedule, a practice he had not been able to follow previously, and he had his best performance in two years. Still another, a world champion, was being forced out of competition by severe side stitches and abdominal sensitivity. He had a seriously weakened diaphragm plus other physical complications. As the muscles of breathing developed, the side stitches and the abdominal pain ceased, and he began taking the hardest workouts he had attempted in years. So it went at Tahoe.

And so it goes with SIMBIC. A whole range of possibilities lies waiting to be explored. Breathing certainly cannot cure any and everything, but breathing coordination has repeatedly indicated its value in relieving the difficulties which arise in other areas of the body. Conversely, faulty breathing can just as readily inflict injury. Whatever, breathing is a body process which will not tolerate neglect.

22

WHERE DANGER LIES

Summer ended abruptly at Tahoe. One bright blue and gold morning I awoke into crisp, cool air which did not get appreciably warmer with the advance of the day. Hardy residents of the high country informed me gleefully that despite the calendar autumn had come upon us. The sudden advent of autumn reminded me that September and the finals were only a matter of days away. The Olympic Executive Committee still had reached no decision on the extension of the SIMBIC project through the finals and on into the Mexican games.

Although the Tahoe staff took my presence for granted and had complete confidence in their recommendations to the Executive Committee, I could not share their certainty. I made a final appeal and waited. This time I did not have to wait long. The reply came promptly with gratitude for the program and regrets that, desirable as the continuation of SIMBIC and my services would be, no more funds were available for that purpose.

When I told my colleagues and pupils of the decision, their shocked response might have been gratifying if I myself had not been quite so concerned over the final competition for positions on the Olympic Team. No one could possibly know what precise effect on breathing problems the tensions and exertion of the last desperate attempt to make the team would have. I surely did not, but I knew the competitors well enough to anticipate their reactions. Some caused me considerable worry and I wanted to be at hand in case they had difficulty in recovery after the exhausting effort to take the coveted honors.

Olympic officials, including Head Coach Payton Jordan and Manager Mike Portanova, assured me that the program extension had been expected as a matter of course and would be a significant contribution if arrangements were possible. The men themselves were requesting SIMBIC sessions in advance of their scheduled events. I felt strongly that I should stay to help the athletes and to observe the effect of the combination of circumstances on their breathing. What I could learn and what I could contribute would warrant an expenditure of Institute funds. On my trip East I had prepared for this eventuality; therefore, the necessary measures could be completed quickly.

Business attended, I went on to more important matters. The approaching competitions strengthened a lot of weak wills, and athletes who had never quite managed to fit SIMBIC into their schedules decided that a little extra measure of security might be worthwhile. Time was too short for the muscles of breathing to develop appreciably, but the men could be taught enough about the management of their breathing to tide them over an emergency. I was amused at this time to learn how much information, as well as misinformation, about breathing had sifted through the athletic strata of Tahoe. Few had failed to renew old error or to adopt new ideas in the wake of SIMBIC. Breathing had become recognized as an essential to top performance.

Sins of omission and commission stood revealed in the remaining days before the finals. The atmosphere was supercharged with tension. Some of the last-minute men came to me wound as tight as toys on Christmas morning and required the better part of the session to get themselves relaxed. Whenever I could, I went up to the track to observe the final workouts. Often while I was there, the wind would swoop down suddenly from over the mountains and kick up swirling clouds of dust in the loose, dry earth surrounding the track. I watched the men battle through those unpredictable flurries and wondered what the direct effect on breathing efficiency might be.

To know where danger lies demands constant vigilance and constant evaluation. Breathing problems can stem just as readily from the quality of the air breathed as from the manner of breathing. Unless an individual is conscious of his breathing pattern, substances in the air he breathes can provoke an alteration in the pattern. Unpleasant fumes induce shallow breathing which easily lapses into accessory breathing with all the attendant problems. Fresh-scented air, identified as "good, clean air," stimulates the desire for deeper inhalations which may or may not be forced. Between the extremes is a scale of responses and potential hazards. The condition of the air itself can never be neglected in considering matters of breathing.

Earlier in the Tahoe season when most of the men had gone down to Los Angeles for sea level competitions, they had expected the removal of the factor of rarefied air at high altitude to provide a certain advantage with resulting improvement in performance. They returned to the mountaintop older and wiser. Their performances had not surpassed those at Tahoe, possibly for many reasons, and the removal of the high altitude air factor had not been the advantage anticipated. All the SIMBIC pupils remarked the restricting effect the air pollution had had on their breathing. Some who experienced little difficulty in recovery at altitude found that the concentrated air pollution of the urban area created recovery problems. Others reported nausea caused by the quality of the air, and some came back with infections. At Tahoe they had been removed from concentrations of pollutants long enough for their respiratory system to become sensitized and to respond with uncommon reaction to the sudden exposure to air pollution.

Danger often lies where least expected. The most serious threat to life in the latter part of the twentieth century is air pollution with its devastating power to alter breathing patterns and render the respiratory system susceptible to functional diseases and disorders which can and do result in fatality. No statistics are kept on the deaths caused directly and indirectly by all the many forms of air pollution. No account is made of the heart attacks provoked by respiratory failure ultimately derived from some unsuspected air pollutant. No count could possibly be taken of the nervous and psychological disorders stimulated by inhaled substances and terminated by suicide. Few ever think of the endless stream of poisons introduced into the body through the air breathed. Breathing problems never stop with the respiratory system alone; they also include the air.

Neither air pollution nor respiratory damage is a new topic. Both have been about for a long, long time. Since the beginning, the winds have been driving dust and sand across the earth, deep commotions within the planet have spewed forth deadly fumes and gases, pollens have floated on the air, and decomposition of organic matter has contributed its noxious share to the surrounding atmosphere. The respiratory system, which makes possible human existence in the atmosphere, is sensitive to and responsive to all that passes through it. Respiratory problems began when the first form of animal life breathed and have been increasing with an accumulative intensity.

For eons the oceans of air enveloping the earth, like the oceans of waters upon the earth, have absorbed and subtly transformed the waste products of the planet. The operation has been a smooth one until the acceleration of waste accumulation by the steady output of civilized society's artificial products. Air pollution is an increasing creation of society which can very well destroy society through destruction of the breathing mechanism as well as the air breathed. The origin of the problem is human greed which refuses to disturb an economic system geared to the production of comforts and conveniences.

Industrial wastes are contaminating the environment faster than ways to counteract them can be conceived much less put into effect. Major offender is the powerful petroleum industry, controller of the lives of billions of people around the earth. Not only do the refineries and allied chemical plants pour out pollutants endlessly, the engines utilizing the products in ever-increasing quantities contribute their deadly share. However, modern economy, spelled with the capital dollar-sign, is so hopelessly allied with industry that the likelihood of diminishing air pollution from this source is at present as remote as the planet Pluto. Individual lives cannot tip the balance of such scales.

Perhaps the sacrifice of enough individual lives to industrial and vehicular wastes may eventually arouse concern and effect change. Meanwhile, respiratory sufferers like the emphysema patient at West Haven who encountered a diesel engine will have to manage their breathing as best they can. For a man in good health to tangle with a machine is risky business. For the emphysema patient the incident was a disaster. The patient had advanced emphysema but with SIMBIC had learned to manage his life efficiently. On a cold day in December he took his car to a garage to have the tires changed, and while he was there waiting, the motor of a trailer truck in for repairs was switched on with the garage doors closed. Before he could escape, he had inhaled the diesel fumes, which set him to coughing. By the time he was outside the building, he was coughing up thick mucus black with diesel exhaust. The cold air made breathing almost impossible for him, and the coughing destroyed his coordination. He was rushed to the hospital by ambulance and arrived in a nearly fatal state of dyspnea.

For three days he coughed up mucus blackened with the adhesive oil particles of the diesel engine fumes. His lungs were highly sensitized and susceptible to infection, and he contracted pneumonia. With SIMBIC we were able to manage his breathing with no problems in that area during his long, debilitating bout with infection. That was the first time in eight years he had had a major illness unaccompanied by an acute breathing problem. Finally, six months after admission to the hospital he was discharged. Although he would never be so listed medically, he was a direct victim of vehicular air pollution. Had he been unable to manage his breathing, he would likely have died.

Air pollution in cities has come to be accepted as part and parcel of urban living. The average city-dweller expects to be victimized by the environmental forces beyond his control. In rural and suburban areas the tendency is to consider air pollution less of a threat. Crop-dusting and pest-control spraying are overlooked as air pollution factors. Those deadly particles are breathed into the lungs and lodge there as irritants while the victims go their merry way wondering at their increased susceptibility to respiratory infection.

On the golf course of a resort hotel I have stood and watched a low-flying plane lay a blanket of insecticide over the hotel grounds as guests continued unheeding with their fun activities. At the first whiff I took shelter indoors, but the others hardly noticed the plane. In the dining room that evening coughs accompanied every course and red eyes were part of the make-up. No one ever knew why a sudden rash of colds appeared in high summer. Nor did anyone suspect that a vicious cycle of respiratory infection and aberrant breathing had been set in motion and could continue indefinitely.

Even more innocently the public has taken unto itself an assortment of individually administered air pollutants in the form of aerosol sprays, certain paints, and household chemicals. Aerosol sprays, introduced on the market in the late 1950's as another step forward to better living, are fine particles of matter suspended in a gas and dispersed into the air under pressure. They are breathed into the lungs and lodge there with all the other inhalants to work their wickedness at the opportune moment. Fumes from paints and household chemicals can be exceedingly dangerous to anyone with a heart condition or a respiratory disorder.

An urban housewife whose heart condition supposedly was under control set about her spring cleaning with a variety of new, improved household products. While cleaning her poorly ventilated bathroom, she was overcome by the fumes resulting from the contact of cleansers and water and had to be hospitalized. The strain of the respiratory reaction further damaged her heart and she never recovered completely from the incident. She continued in a semi-invalid state for a number of months and finally died of complications of her heart condition. If records were carefully kept and could be carefully examined, statistics would be shocking.

King of all the self-administered air pollutants is tobacco smoke. If smokers damaged only themselves, that would be matter enough for concern. However, the manners of the modern smoker are barbaric, and the barbarism is aided and abetted by public institutions. The smoker who pauses to give so much as a passing thought to the non-smoker is fast disappearing from the earth. The non-smoker, whatever his desire or respiratory condition, has become the trapped, unwilling victim of the smoker. The tars and nicotine may have filtered through the smoker's lungs, but the expelled smoke is unavoidably inhaled by the non-smoker and can and does irritate the respiratory passages. Should a state of sensitivity exist, a non-smoker's respiratory system can become so irritated by expelled smoke that respiratory infection is readily contracted. Such considerations would appear to be ignored by operators of the public services. The few existing no-smoking regulations are laxly enforced.

Soaring aloft with absolutely no avenue of escape, the air traveler is forced to inhale directly the smoke of the passengers around him, and through the inadequate air conditioning system he must inhale an admixture of all the smoke of all the smokers. Woe be unto him if the lot includes a cigar or pipe smoker. But who cares for his burning eyes and aching throat and chest? Certainly not the airlines, nor the railroads, nor the buses, nor restaurateurs, nor anyone else in business.

Air pollution is something that happens to the air outside, so goes the myth.

Outside, inside, wherever it is, air pollution is air pollution. Men, women, and children, smokers and non-smokers, have to breathe air. If air pollution continues at its present giddying pace, respiratory problems can be expected to mount. All the products for the artificial needs of a progressive society will not be able to repair damaged lung tissue nor to restore weakened muscles of breathing. Progress comes at a high price.

An effective personal measure to counteract exposure to air pollution is the prolonged exhale, once the safety of uncontaminated or relatively uncontaminated air has been reached. It helps to move air through the lungs and prevent the build-up of irritants in the respiratory passages. Nothing can substitute for clean air, but effective breathing habits can be of great advantage in the maintenance of health in spite of air pollution.

23

THE CRYSTAL BALL

September tipped the tall pines with golden light beneath blue, wind-swept skies for the 1968 Olympic Team Trials at South Lake Tahoe. Excitement and expectation snapped and crackled through the air like a charge of electricity. The time had come. Across the finish tape lay Mexico City with all its glitter of glory, and this was the opportunity to get there ahead of the crowd.

South Lake Tahoe swarmed with newsmen carrying tiny typewriters, radio and television commentators trailing truckloads of broadcasting equipment, manufacturers' representatives bestowing all sorts of products which might be remotely connected with athletic endeavor and later so advertised as used by the Olympic Team. Observers from other countries joined the sports enthusiasts from down below to form a cheering throng of spectators. The schedule of events and the conditions surrounding the trials reproduced as nearly as possible the conditions which might be expected in Mexico City so that the team candidates could have a foretaste of the real thing.

The easy atmosphere which had enveloped the workouts and competitions of the summer vanished when the visitors began to arrive. A certain purpose reflected in the eyes of the

Dr. Breath

athletes, and the magic sound of "Mexico" was heard at every turn. SIMBIC pupils were participating in fourteen of the events, and my schedule of pre-event sessions hardly left me time to get up to the track for the trials. No one but the athletes themselves knew what personal challenge the trials held for them. To judge by body tensions, for many the days of the trials would mark a turning point; for some the trials would become finals indeed. For all, the pressures were excessive.

Each day after my early SIMBIC sessions I hurried to the track to be ready to cope with the unpredictable. Psychological tensions generated by the desperate desire to win a place on the team created body responses which were manifest immediately in the breathing. Men who had had no problem in the practice competitions of the summer experienced difficulties under the extreme stress and greater exertion of the team trials. Athletes who were not in the SIMBIC program and who had not learned to manage their breathing efficiently had difficulties far in excess of those of the SIMBIC men.

Athletes who had breathing coordination sessions prior to competitions reported a greater ease of performance than those who did not. Rick Sloan was a singular example. At the end of the first day of the decathlon trials he was in fifth place and had incurred a serious oxygen debt in the four-hundred-meters. Following the race I worked with him for about an hour or so to bring him round, and that evening he continued to concentrate on his breathing. The second day he made certain between each event that his breathing was properly coordinated. In the course of the day he moved spectacularly from fifth place in the competition to second place on the decathlon team. The improvement in his performance he credited to his ability to manage his breathing.

A high point in the trials for me was Lee Evans' victory in

240

the four-hundred-meters. Lee came into the SIMBIC program late in the season because of a breathing problem which produced a burning sensation in his chest. He developed at a remarkable pace and was able to eliminate the burning sensation when he ran. In the early rounds of the trials he was pitted against close competition, but he went on to the finals to first place on the team.

Despite all the excitement and flurry of newsmen and cameramen clustering about him after his winning race, he remembered SIMBIC and told the press that his breathing had influenced his performance. Such expansiveness of spirit meant a great deal to me personally and a great deal to the education program which is an important part of the SIMBIC Institute. Ironically, the statement of one athlete whom SIMBIC has aided in a winning performance can do more to make the public aware of the importance of proper breathing habits than can scores of testimonials of emphysema patients who owe their very lives to their acquired ability to manage their breathing. Later, when I thanked Lee for his courtesy, he assured me that anything he could do for the SIMBIC program he would do gladly.

Performances in the Tahoe trials were stellar and were cheered uproariously by the spectators and lauded by the press. With all the glory around the track no one noticed the agony in the green recovery tent. The men were exerting themselves to the limit of endurance. Oxygen debt was inevitable, but the men who had had SIMBIC instruction were able to manage their breathing and, with help, recovered in comparatively short time. Often, after the games had ended for the day, I was still in the recovery tent working an athlete out of an oxygen debt and preventing the administration of oxygen by enthusiastic ambulance corpsmen. Had oxygen been administered to any one of the men at that point, the consequences could have been serious. In oxygen debt the need is to clear the lungs of carbon dioxide. Indiscriminate administration of oxygen holds the potential of suffocation. Forcing oxygen into lungs already overextended with unexpelled air can be of no advantage, but the point is frequently wasted on the uninformed who believe oxygen debt simply to mean lack of oxygen.

For the Olympic Team Trials the staff of the Medical Testing and Study Program was replaced by the staff that would accompany the team to Mexico. None of the coaches, trainers, or doctors had been present at Tahoe at the time the several SIMBIC lecture-demonstrations were presented, and none was familiar enough with the mechanics of breathing and management of breathing crises to deal expertly with problem recoveries. This knowledge coupled with an awareness of the air pollution in Mexico City was not calculated to comfort me. I knew further that the ultimate competition for Olympic medals would hold tensions and pressures and exertions to make the Tahoe Trials seem like a little girls' skipping contest.

The course of the summer's work with the Olympic candidates had left me with a sense of responsibility for the welfare of the athletes in the SIMBIC program. At the trials I was called upon to manage the breathing problems of men who were not in the program; so, my feeling of responsibility gradually spilled out over the entire team. There was not the remotest possibility by this time that Olympic funds would be channeled into breathing recovery problems in Mexico City, but there was every chance that the Institute could finance such an enterprise as a service project for the U.S. Olympic Committee if I could obtain the credentials necessary to admit me to the track and the restricted areas of the competitions in Mexico City. Loyally backed by the Olympic personnel and the athletes, who could not believe that I would not be with them indefinitely, I busied about trying to get credentials.

Meanwhile, the trials continued to knock down old records and establish new ones. The performances were truly Olympian, some almost beyond belief. Mighty deeds were done in those bright September days. The competitions were difficult for me because I knew the men and their ambitions, and they could not all win even though I wished they might. To lose is sad when winning can mean so much. Because a number of Olympic candidates had spent the summer working out elsewhere than Tahoe, new elements of competition appeared at the trials, frequently with surprising results. Athletes who had been expected to win easily did not always fulfill the high expectations.

At the outset of the SIMBIC program eight events requiring sustained exertion of two minutes and over were designated for inclusion; however, in time coaches in six other events requested that men with breathing problems be instructed. Of the fourteen events represented, SIMBIC pupils were winners in eleven and placed fourth in the other three. The entire decathlon, eight-hundred-meters, and fifty-kilo walk teams were made up of SIMBIC pupils: Bill Toomey, Rick Sloan, and Tom Waddell of the decathlon; Tom Farrell, Wade Bell, and Ron Kutschinski of the eight-hundred-meters; and Larry Young, Goetz Klopfer, and Dave Romansky of the fifty-kilo walk.

In the twenty-kilo walk SIMBIC pupils Ron Laird and Tom Dooley placed first and third; in the long jump Phil Shinnick was fourth; in the three-thousand-meter steeplechase Bob Price came in fourth; in the four-hundred-meter intermediate hurdles Boyd Gittins and Ron Whitney were second and third; in the four-hundred-meters Lee Evans and Ron Freeman took first and third; in the one-hundred-ten-meter high hurdles Pat Pomphrey ran fourth; in the pole vault John Pennel placed second; in the two-hundred-meters John Carlos was first; in the fifteen-hundred-meters Marty Liquori and Dave Patrick were second and fourth; in the triple jump Art Walker placed first; in the five-thousand-meters Lou Scott and Gerry Lindgren ran third and fourth.

The outcome of the trials pleased me very much because the SIMBIC winners enthusiastically acknowledged the influence of breathing on their performance, and like Lee Evans' statement to the press, such acknowledgment from champions goes a long way toward persuading the average citizen that he might do well to look to his breathing. All in all, the summer had been exceptionally rewarding to me. I had had an opportunity to perform a greatly needed service for the United States Olympic Committee and simultaneously to gather a quantity of valuable information for use of the Institute in the future. Moreover, I had come to know and to appreciate many people engaged in an activity with which I had had previously only a nodding acquaintance.

In spite of the plus factors of the trials, I still had troubling minuses to consider. The extreme effort the athletes had exerted to win their places on the Olympic Team had precipitated oxygen debt requiring my aid in the management of recovery. I had helped men in the decathlon, in the eight-hundred-meters, and in the five-thousand-meters. Four had severe recovery problems which were resolved in relatively short time. I was not happy at the thought of their being unaided in Mexico City. In case I failed to get credentials for the Mexican games, I worked out a plan with Dr. Tom Waddell of the decathlon team whereby he could supervise the breathing and the athletes could help one another with their recovery problems. I urged him especially to avoid the use of oxygen in oxygen debt recovery. I had complete confidence in Tom's knowledge and judgment and felt much better with him in charge.

Back at the old waiting game again wondering whether my credentials for Mexico City would come through, I made a mental note of the great need for research into the effect on the respiratory system of extreme exertion in combination with such factors as heat and air pollution both at time of exertion and afterward. My mental note reminded me that I had better get out the crystal ball and take a look into the future of the Institute. The experiences of the summer had brought to the fore many possibilities for both service and research. As soon as the last report on the Olympics had been written and the mountain of data sorted and correlated and filed, new projects should be ready for exploration and evaluation. Coaches and athletes had made numerous suggestions for work in athletics alone, and my broadening range of observation had made me especially conscious of the need for such practical projects as the service program for the Olympic Committee as well as abstract research projects into the effects and implications of breathing coordination.

The SIMBIC Institute is a young, evolving organization operating in an area so taken for granted that mustering serious consideration for it is a wearyingly difficult task. Otherwise intelligent people often respond very foolishly to matters of breathing until they encounter a respiratory problem or experience dyspnea. One of the objectives of the Institute is to concern the public with the constantly enlarging need for proper breathing management to combat the effects of air pollution on the respiratory system and on the total efficiency of the body functions. No one, whatever his physical condition, can afford any longer to ignore or to take lightly his mode of breathing. Everyone, even top athletes, can improve the efficiency of breathing.

Although the Institute is a tax-exempt, non-profit organization for research and education in the field of breathing, it has access only to limited funds for application to immediate projects. The policy has been to seek funds for current needs, not to accrue against future possibilities. As the Institute grows, the policy will adapt to the climate of the time.

The ultimate goal is the establishment of a respiratory center for the diagnosis and management of problems of breathing, for development of SIMBIC practitioners, and for SIMBIC instruction on a broader scale than is possible at present. Research eventually may yield methods of teaching SIMBIC on other than an individual basis; meanwhile, the sole known way of establishing breathing coordination is with the aid of a skilled instructor to make the pupil aware of body responses to his individualistic pattern of breathing. Before SIMBIC can become available generally, a system of developing practitioners must be evolved. SIMBIC instruction is a complex process which cannot be undertaken without extensive preparation. The ultimate goal has to be approached as a journey through time. Always it lies at the center of the crystal ball to challenge the imagination and the fortitude.

Until the future becomes the present, much research waits to be done. Little is known of the effect of breathing patterns in the practice of psychiatry or in the management of nervous disorders, drug addiction, circulatory disorders, and the like. The value of proper breathing in prophylaxis is known, but methods of application need to be evolved, particularly in such areas as public schools and athletic programs. Knowledge is limited in regard to the effects of inhalants on the efficiency of mental and physical functions, the influence of fluctuations in the rate of breathing, and the inter-effects of the respiratory system and the other systems of the body. Wherever a breathing problem is in evidence, a need for investigation exists. The Institute proposes to highlight the needs and to fulfill them insofar as is possible.

The problem of what to do has never troubled the Institute. The question has always been which project to undertake next. As I hovered over the crystal ball trying to divert my thoughts from the Olympics by probing into the future, some business matters arose in Southern California and the Southwest, and the time came to leave Tahoe. Coasting down the other side of the Sierra, I wished mightily that my mythical crystal ball would give me a glimpse of what lay ahead in the immediate weeks to come. It remained quite unrevealing.

24

DR. BREATH
TURNS THE LAST STONE

After the autumnal chill of Tahoe and the unperturbable heights of the Sierra, the warmth and bustle of Southern California were pleasant contrast. Like a hermit in from the hills, I had to accustom myself to the abrupt change of surroundings. Fortunately, my business affairs were uncomplicated and permitted the indulgence in a brief holiday to celebrate the conclusion of the summer's tasks. However, nagging at the back of my mind were the probabilities of Mexico City: what might happen, what would be done, how breathing problems might be avoided. I did not feel that I had the answer to all things in the respiratory category, but I knew that I did have solutions for many problems likely to occur.

During my excursion across the Southwest over a terrain sharply reminiscent of Mexico, I could not shake off the conviction that someone thoroughly familiar with the operation of the respiratory system and with the numerous complications of breathing in the crucial period of recovery from extreme exertion should be at hand for the Olympic games. Those eventful moons ago at Yale when I was smiling at the emergence of "Dr. Breath," I should never have thought that the same Dr. Breath, then wholly absorbed in the abstracts of breathing, could so involve himself in the realities of sports competition.

He had, however, and in the process had charged too many windmills and turned too many stones along the way to leave a stone unturned now. Very little action was possible out in the middle of the great American desert, but back in New York I had a few final resources to try before resigning the effort. My sense of urgency surprised me. I thought I had come to terms with that by-product of the intensity of the work at Tahoe, the assumption of personal responsibility for the welfare of the athletes, but still it plagued me.

My return to New York at the end of September brought me into an inheritance of inquiries from all over the country. The finals at Tahoe and the impending Mexican games had precipitated a quantity of SIMBIC publicity and had drawn attention to breathing. When athletes supposedly in the finest of physical condition attest their need for proper breathing measures, the average citizen at last begins to reckon that he might do with a few improvements. The mail was filled with every conceivable request and a few I should never have imagined. Projects suggested by enterprising promoters would have filled several calendars. In among the oddities were a number of serious proposals for cooperative research and enough earnest queries to underscore further the need for public education in the field of breathing and the functions of the respiratory system.

One piece of correspondence was of singular import. It closed the final door on the hope that I might obtain credentials for the Mexican Olympics through the United States Olympic Committee. At the time the credentials had been allotted, there was no category for me, and the United States quota had been filled long since. As the quota had been uncommonly large from the outset, other participating countries were a trifle testy about the matter. Nevertheless, I decided to approach the International Committee with the suggestion that my services be made available on an international basis and that I not be considered a United States representative.

By then September had given way to October and the games were only days away. When I conferred with President Avery Brundage's staff, the International Committee was embroiled in crises threatening the opening of the Olympics. My suggestion was welcomed, but at that point the acquisition of credentials lay with the Mexican Organizing Committee. Being thus advised, I immediately made an appointment with the Mexican Consul in New York. Consul Pesquerie received me graciously and listened with mounting enthusiasm while I explained my proposal: In a gesture of international goodwill the SIMBIC Institute would make my services as a respiratory consultant available to anyone requiring them in the course of the games. He felt certain that credentials would present no problem.

Although I knew better than to be certain of anything unaccomplished, I did permit myself a moment of optimism just to relieve the suspense which seemed to permeate my activities. Before the Consul could complete the transaction for me, he became involved in affairs of state and advised direct communication with President Pedro Ramírez Vázquez of the Mexican Olympic Organizing Committee. He gave his complete endorsement of the proposal and assured me of his full support.

As October 12, the opening date, crept ever closer, I was busy on the telephone and telegraph wires to Mexico City. Finally all the red tape was cleared. My honest intentions were defined unmistakably. Dr. Breath had turned the last stone, and as usual, nothing remained to be done but to wait. I was glad there was not much time for that, but even so, the intensity made up for the duration. When the determining telegram from Mexico arrived, I realized that, whatever the message, nothing could disturb my sense of relief. I had done all that I could do.

Couched in graceful, diplomatic terms, President Vázquez's telegram thanked me for the offer and explained that the credentials list, closed before my application, could not be reopened. I read the telegram a second time and tested my response. I was still relieved to have a final decision. Now I could lay aside my self-imposed responsibility and go on to the next thing.

Long before I left Tahoe, I had decided not to make the trip to Mexico City unless I could be of service to the athletes. I could not sit in the stadium and watch the games knowing that I was powerless to give the help needed. Being so near and yet so far was a condition beyond my endurance. I was certain that the SIMBIC men could manage their breathing efficiently during recovery and, in the unfailing generosity of the athletic code, would help others. But generous intent and professional skill are not the same. If I could not go to Mexico to employ my professional skill, I should have to absent myself from the scene. In the early days of Tahoe I had tried the casual bystander role unsuccessfully. I did not propose to put myself through that nerve-racking experience again.

On Saturday, October 12, 1968, amid much pomp and circumstance, the Olympics began without me—without my bodily presence, that is. I had laid out a heavy schedule of work for myself to try to catch up on some of the formidable accumulation during my extended absence. The schedule was also for the purpose of diverting my thoughts from Mexico City, but it failed. After a feeble struggle I gave up all pretense of work and took up my station before the television set. The end of every competition involving SIMBIC men found me pacing the floor, coaching, advising, cajoling, imploring, hoping the athletes would avoid the oxygen tanks constantly and dramatically presented on the television screen. For all my knowledge of SIMBIC, I was not certain that my own respiratory system could have withstood the tensions and pressures of on-the-scene witness of those monumental events. As a would-be spectator, I should likely have been driven to madness and attempted to battle through the guards to aid the athletes. Again, I congratulated myself on having the good sense to remain in New York with adequate mileage between myself and circumstances beyond my control.

My trackside view of the Olympics on television left me limp. I ran and jumped for everybody and tried to breathe for them all. I had my moments of supreme elation, though, when Bill Toomey placed first in the decathlon and Lee Evans and Ron Freeman swept through the four-hundred-meters with first and third. Achievements of the other bronze-medal men—Tom Farrell in the eight-hundred-meters, John Carlos in the two-hundred-meters, and Larry Young in the fifty-kilo walk—accorded me like pleasure. I did not delude myself that SIMBIC makes athletes. Great athletes are compounded of iron will, courage, and a few other uncommon qualities as well as muscle, bone, and nerve. They make themselves. I was glad that SIMBIC could help them do the job and assist in repairs after competition.

When the 1968 Olympics concluded, I came to the end of an era. I was about a thousand years older and considerably wiser than at the outset of my investigation of the breathing

habits and patterns of the physically superior. Dr. Breath had
gone forth naïvely in search of perfection and had come home
from the adventure with a bagful of pieces to be fitted into the
puzzling complex of human breathing. Teaching SIMBIC is an
exchange process wherein the instructor can learn much from
the pupil, for each pupil is unique and makes his unique response. The athletes, from the Boys' Clubs through the Yale
men on to the Olympians, had taught me more about the
application of SIMBIC than they might have guessed.

Apart from the professional rewards of the Olympic project, I derived much personal satisfaction from the friendships
and acquaintances which grew along the Tahoe trail. I had
been thoroughly initiated into the sports world and would continue to follow athletic careers as a matter of personal as well
as professional interest. Sooner or later everyone came to Madison Square Garden, and I would be there to watch the performance and check the breathing for any faults which might
have developed.

The wake of the Olympics brought official expressions of
gratitude for the SIMBIC program. Everett D. Barnes, acting
executive director for the United States Olympic Committee,
wrote: "The work that has been accomplished and the interest you have shown in the program are deeply appreciated.
Please accept our thanks." USOC President Douglas F. Roby
cited SIMBIC with "We wish to thank you for your interest and
we trust that the results of the work you have done will encourage the United States Olympic Committee to follow a
program as recommended by you in the future."

From Dr. Merritt Stiles, who was responsible for intro-
ducing the SIMBIC project to the USOC originally, came the
assurance: "I recommend strongly that our athletes continue

to work with you, to whatever extent you can handle. Thanks again for your great help."

Payton Jordan, head coach of the 1968 U.S. Olympic Track and Field Team, was cordial in his comments: "Even though I did express my 'thanks' verbally to you for your unselfish contributions to our 1968 'team' effort at the time of the Tahoe Altitude Training, I want to express in writing my eternal gratitude for your personal friendship and your expert breathing coordination instruction for the athletes. On behalf of every athlete, our coaching and managerial staff, we wish to share with you the fine successes enjoyed at Mexico City. You were instrumental in creating the finest spirit ever and more World and Olympic records than in all past Games history! I extend my best wishes to you for continued fine success."

Among my prized possessions is the Mexican Olympic commemorative coin mounted in a key chain from Mike Portanova, manager for the U.S. Olympic Track and Field Team. Mike and I shared some tense moments during the Tahoe trials, and he became an enthusiastic exponent of breathing coordination.

Although the Mexican games marked the end of the 1968 Olympic adventures of Dr. Breath, I somehow had the feeling that he was not yet entirely finished with the athletes. The winds of Tahoe had stirred up a lot of ideas along with the dust. After the records and materials were sorted and the reports written and all the papers filed neatly away, Dr. Breath just might be off and running again. I wondered what Gieg and the Yale men would say to that.

A Note About the Author

Carl Stough was born in 1926 in York, Pennsylvania, and now lives in New York City. He is married and has one daughter. His wife is co-author of this book.